THE BATH BOOK

THE

BATH BOOK

By GREGORY and BEVERLY FRAZIER

Illustrations by Bruce W. Martin

TROUBADOR PRESS SAN FRANCISCO

Published in San Francisco by Troubador Press
Printed in the United States of America

Library of Congress Catalog Card Number: 72-92941
ISBN: 0-912300-38-8 (Softbound)
ISBN: 0-912300-37-X (Hardbound)

TROUBADOR PRESS
126 Folsom Street
San Francisco, CA 94105

For
Thomas E. Frazier,
a plumber

ACKNOWLEDGEMENTS

We gratefully acknowledge the professional assistance of May Dichiera, Registered Physical Therapist, San Francisco; Sven G. Lund, Sven's Sauna, Mill Valley and Dr. K. C. Petersen, The Cosmetic Chemist, Berkeley, California. In addition, we sincerely thank all the other friends who gave their assistance and encouragement.

CONTENTS

FOREWORD

Throughout the ages, the bath has had its alternating periods of popularity and decline. In our time, the hygienic necessity of bathing and cleanliness is a foregone conclusion. Most of us bathe regularly and pride ourselves on clean living. The problem is that many of us bathe for cleanliness *only*, letting the more aesthetic aspects of the bath go down the drain.

It is our intention not to dwell on the obvious hygienic necessity of bathing, but instead to emphasize the delights and pleasures of the bath.

Our accelerated pace of living leaves us little time for a tranquil soak in a hot tub. Moreover, bathing has become a chore; a bothersome task, squeezed in between 5:15 and cocktails. The leisurely, relaxing bath is being abandoned in favor of the quick, invigorating shower. We would suggest a compromise wherein the bath and the shower both be utilized for their unique advantages. Just as the shower has its place in the scheme of things, so should the bath be afforded the time it so richly deserves. Or, put another way, *you should afford yourself the time you so richly deserve.*

We hope by increasing your knowledge and awareness of the bath, to enhance your enjoyment of it. Steep your body in a steaming tub, float away tensions, drown anxieties, relax...enjoy.

Gregory and Beverly Frazier
San Francisco

A BATH FOR ALL TIMES

THE BATH PRIMEVAL

No one knows when bathing for cleanliness
originated. We can reasonably assume, however,
that the refreshing properties
of water
were known to early man from the very
beginning of his existence.

Primitive implements, dating back to the Stone Age and the dawn of history, are found mainly on the banks of rivers, streams and other natural watering places. Prehistoric man built shelters on the river banks to be close to his source of life-giving water. Outside the front door, cool running water cleared the dust of the hunt from his throat and carried away all traces of his waste. He soaked in sun-drenched pools and springs, fragrant with earth's freshest scents. Pine, jasmine and lotus floated on the waters, sweetening the bath primeval. Falling rains and waterfalls, cool and invigorating, were his first shower baths. Like modern man, the primitive emerged from his improvised bath refreshed and ready to resume the struggle for survival. The fact that he was "clean" was probably incidental to his thinking, if, indeed, he thought at all about the cleansing properties of water. Prehistoric cave paintings give no portrayal of bathing or washing.

Beauty sat bathing by a spring
  Where fairest shades did hide her;
The winds blew calm, the birds did sing,
  The cool streams ran beside her.
                    — Anthony Munday

In time man ventured beyond the narrow confines of his waterside villages in a wider search for food in his expanding universe. He carried the water with him in crude vessels. The further he ventured from the water's source, the more valuable it became. Left behind was the luxury of the tranquil forest pool. Water was strictly for drinking — and later for cultivation. Bathing was a waste of water, and taboo.

During this early period of man's history, many mystical and religious attributes were ascribed to water, as they were to other natural phenomena such as fire and the heavenly bodies. Precious water became holy water, a divine gift to be revered and respected.

To treat water carelessly was to invite the wrath of the spirits and the condemnation of the community. Even today, some primitive societies, like the Australian aborigines, believe their water holes to be sacred.

Ablution, the ritual use of water, should not be confused with bathing. Ablution cleans the spirit, but not necessarily the flesh. The "stains" caused by "unclean" contacts—persons of inferior caste, the dead, diseased, insane, and others—are "cleansed" by ablution. It is believed that ablution originated with the ancient Hebrews when it was practiced by both priests and laity. Water purification ceremonies are described in the Old Testament and the *Koran.* Faithful Mohammedans still observe the washing ritual before prayer. The Catholic priest washes his fingers after communion in continuation of an age old rite. By washing his hands, Pontius Pilate absolved himself—and Rome—of the guilt of Christ's crucifixion. If the water is blessed, its purifying powers are increased. Baptism by water is a sacrament in many of the world's religions. The Nile is sacred to the Egyptians; the Ganges to the Hindus. The 15th century Knights of the Bath were ceremoniously bathed before being dubbed, not for cleanliness of the body, but purity of the spirit.

Bathing became more widespread when man was able to transport large quantities of water from its source to his distant villages. Initially, water was carried to reservoirs by human slaves. Later it was transported by primitive pipe systems. Since only the wealthy could command slaves or afford to construct pipe systems, bathing was a luxury reserved for kings and nobles. Not until much later in history did the bath become available to the common man.

It is not known exactly when the first bathroom was built. One discovered in India is estimated to be 6000 years old; another is believed to have been built by the ancient Babylonians some 5000 years ago. The Egyptians were enjoying showers as early as 3000 B.C.

The earliest known bathrooms in recorded history originated in Minoan Crete around 1700 B.C., where a magnificent palace was constructed for King Minos at Knossos. Daedalus, the mythical Greek architect and sculptor, was said to have designed the palace. As sanitary engineers, the Minoans showed remarkable skill in the construction of their bathrooms and bathing facilities. Terra-cotta pipes unearthed at Knossos are almost 4000 years old. The palace had its own drainage systems which were flushed by rain water. Although the bath water had to be carried into the palace by hand, drains were provided to carry it away. A handsomely painted terra-cotta bathtub found at the palace is believed to have belonged to the queen. The Minoans displayed equal sophistication in the construction of their elaborate public baths.

Other ancient bathrooms date to approximately the same period. In the Indus Valley, bathrooms with water-flushed toilets were built between 2500 and 1500 B.C. Bathrooms found at Mari in Syria are dated to 2000 B.C. Around 1500 B.C., bathrooms appeared in neo-Babylon and Mesopotamia where many of the pipes,

And behold, the daughter of Pharaoh came down to wash herself in the river: and her maids walked in the river's brink. And when she saw the basket in the sedges, she sent one of her maids for it...

— Exodus II:5

sewers and toilets are still functioning as if built yesterday. In spite of the fact that many early Egyptian palaces contained bathrooms and bathing facilities, some authorities believe that baths did not exist in Egypt until after the birth of Moses. They base their conclusion on Exodus, which tells us that Pharaoh and his daughters bathed in the Nile. Moses, in Egyptian, means "one taken out of the water."

Many of the ancient civilizations of the Fertile Crescent also used perfumes and cosmetics in great quantities. In terms of hygiene, they were equal, if not superior, to modern man. They bathed for cleanliness and practiced the cosmetic arts to make themselves more attractive to others. But it wasn't until the glory of Greece and the grandeur of Rome that the pleasures of the bath reached their full classical splendor.

THE CLASSICAL BATH

In the highly developed culture of ancient Greece, water was prized as a health-giving gift from the gods. The Greek's love of water and bathing is celebrated in their literature, art and architecture. Homer makes frequent mention of bathing in his epics, telling us that visitors to Greek households were offered a bath, followed by an anointing with aromatic oils. Bathing is a common subject of Grecian vase paintings, which also depict shower baths. A famous classical statue captures Aphrodite in a frozen moment, eternally surprised at her bath. Temples built in honor of Aesculapius, the god of medicine, were located near natural watering places. Hot sulphur springs were the ancient counterparts of the modern health spas. Natural spring waters were believed to contain the same magical health-giving minerals found in certain herbs and stones. Steam baths were known to the Greeks as early as the 6th Century B.C.

Bathing played an important role in the lives of the ancient Greeks, but it never reached the luxuriousness of the later Roman baths. The Greek bath was an addendum to the gymnasium, where it was given only limited space. Quick and cold, it was designed to stimulate athletes before the games. Homer mentions hot baths, but Hesiod dismisses them as unmanly. The rugged Spartans were the first Greeks to follow a cold bath with a warm one. The warm bath was borrowed from the eastern nations whose sumptuous baths Alexander had admired. Unlike the Greek gymnasia, the Spartan version was co-ed, with both men and women sharing the field and the bath. Athletic contests were performed in the nude by glistening, oiled athletes, and were followed by warm relaxing baths. It is believed that private dwelling baths were uncommon in Greece until after 400 B.C., even though public bathhouses with exercise rooms flourished in Athens at that time.

The ancient Romans, with their organizational genius and love of luxury, developed the art of bathing to a scope and refinement unequaled until recent times. They left a string of magnificent baths throughout the known world from Britain to Africa. Their water-carrying and drainage systems are among the most sophisticated ever constructed. Clay sewage pipes laid by the ancient Romans are still in use today in modern Rome.

During the Monarchy and early Republic, public and private bathing were confined to the Tiber, its tributaries, and other natural bodies of water. It was the custom to wash only the arms and legs. The entire body was bathed only once every nine days, on market day. Cleanliness was incidental to bathing.

Due to the hilly terrain of Rome, it wasn't until 441 years after the city's foundation that water was conveyed to its interior through aqueducts. Eventually thirteen aqueducts were completed. Several *thermae* (baths) were constructed throughout Rome. These early baths were not nearly as elaborate as those to follow, however. In 21 B.C., the first public bath was built by Agrippa.

**He really bathes
In a large gilded tub, and steeps his feet
And legs in rich Egyptian unguents;
His jaws and breast he rubs with thick palm oil,
And both his arms with extract sweet of mint;
His eyebrows and his hair with marjoram,
His knees and neck with essence of ground thyme.
— *Antiphanes***

Near the decline of the Republic, baths were attached to the gymnasia in the Greek style. As physicians began prescribing water treatment for the ailments of their patients, the baths increased rapidly in popularity and number, becoming more luxurious in the process. During the reign of Caesar Augustus, the first *calida piscina* or "swimming bath" was built. This huge bathtub was supplied with warm water and heralded the bathing rage that followed. The Roman state officially promoted the establishment of public baths and subsidized their construction. The best architectural and artistic skills were applied to the baths, both inside and out. They were ancient pleasure domes, built with many small chambers sur-

---

To such a pitch of luxury we have reached that we are dissatisfied if we do not tread on gems in our baths.

— Seneca

---

rounding a large central hall. In addition to hot, cold and steam baths, they contained meeting halls, libraries, theaters, art galleries, temples and exercise rooms. Romans of all classes mixed freely beneath vaulted, gilded and painted ceilings. One could stroll along mosaic pavements past marble columns and tubs, numerous statues, bas-reliefs, vases and other precious art objects.

The colossal baths of Caracalla, built in 217 A.D., measured 1100 square feet and could accommodate close to 2000 bathers in 25 different kinds of baths. Some 3000 separate bath recesses might accommodate six bathers each, so that theoretically up to 18,000 people could bathe simultaneously. No less extravagant were the baths of Diocletian, constructed in 302 A.D. Like the Caracalla baths, they were constructed of concrete and their remains have survived to modern times. At the height of the period, in the 4th century A.D., Rome boasted 11 public baths, 1352 public fountains and cisterns, and 856 private baths. Three hundred gallons of water were provided for each Roman per day. In contemporary San Francisco, the per capita average is 145 gallons per day, including industrial use.

Communal life centered around the baths, which were the great social gathering places of the day. In earlier times, mixed bathing was unknown: a father and son could not even share the same bath, and respectable women never visited the *thermae*. In Imperial Rome, the *balnea mixta* or "mixed bath" came into vogue. Bath attendants were of the opposite sex and promiscuity was rampant in and around the limpid pools. Emperor Hadrian closed the mixed baths early in the 2nd century A.D.

Baths, wine, and Venus
   bring decay to our bodies,
But baths, wine, and Venus
   make life worth living.
                         —Anon

The *thermae* were open from 1 P.M. until dark. At one o'clock a bell sounded, indicating that the water was hot. The bather paid his *quadrans* to enter and proceeded to the *apodyterium*. There he undressed with the aid of an attendant before passing into the *unctuarium*, a heated room where his body was rubbed all over with oil. Now he was ready for the *sphaeristerium*, an exercise room which was artifically heated when not warmed by the sun. After some wrestling or a game of tennis to raise a good sweat, he went to the *calidarium*. The *calidarium* or hot room provided steam and hot baths. At this point in the complicated process his body was scraped of oil and perspiration with curved metal *strigiles*. After the scraping, he was given a thorough massage, then doused with water to remove all remaining traces of dirt. Next came the *tepidarium* for a lukewarm rinse before entering the *frigidarium* for a cold plunge. Finally, he returned to the *unctuarium* for the last rub of the bathing ritual. There the hearty Roman was dried, manicured, and again oiled and perfumed with the finest, most costly fragrances. He came out smelling like a rose after spending five of the most luxurious hours in bathing history. And only incidentally was he clean!

The decline of the Roman bath was concurrent with the fall of the Roman Empire. The barbarian hordes that conquered Rome in the 4th century A.D. saw the glorious baths as symbols of Roman decadence. They scoffed the Romans as effeminate and softened by luxury. Destruction, disuse and decay doomed the baths in Europe for almost 1000 years.

THE BATH MEDIEVAL

To the uncouth barbarians in the early part of the Middle Ages, bathing was a necessary evil to be endured only infrequently—if at all—and merely for health and cleanliness. Bathing as a sensuous pleasure never occurred to these simple people. Medieval etiquette books recommended washing the hands before eating, but only because there were no forks. Bathing went unmentioned.

The most primitive sanitary conditions prevailed, even in castles and palaces, although most royalty had at least one portable bathtub. Private baths were available at inns. Water had to be heated on a wood fire and carried to the bathing chamber, usually located in the bedroom. After bathing, the water had to be carried out again. Modesty was unknown. Families and guests shared the same bed chambers, slept in the nude, and often bathed in mixed company. It was a cozy time, but not noted for its cleanliness.

King John of England is said to have bathed at least once every three weeks. The Danes were thought eccentric for bathing every Saturday. In 1399, Henry IV formed the Order of the Bath, thus assuring that his knights would bathe at least once in their life as part of the dubbing ceremony. Queen Isabella of Castile boasted that she'd had only two baths in her lifetime; one at birth, the other at marriage.

Public bathing was reintroduced into Europe by knights returning from the eastern Crusades. The communal Turkish baths borrowed by the Crusaders were similar to the Roman *thermae*. Set in Moorish and Byzantine style architecture, they consisted of a series of warm, hot and steam rooms roughly corresponding to the *tepidarium* and *calidarium*. A basin of cold water replaced the Roman *frigidarium*. Also replaced was the Roman use of the baths as places of exercise and culture. To the weary bathers of Islam, the baths were a place to rest, nap, smoke and sip Turkish coffee.

To the Crusaders, they were welcome additions to a nearly waterless world.

In Europe, the Turkish baths were called "stews," and bathing was "stewing." Stews were quite common in the 12th century. By the 14th and 15th centuries they were notorious as hothouses of vice. Prostitutes openly exhibited their wares. Gambling was rampant. Promiscuity once again became the rage of the continent. In Italy, the stews were called *bordellos* and *bagnios*, words of ill repute ever since. Obviously, the stews were popular meeting places. They were most crowded in the early morning hours, when men and women, youths and maidens, nuns and monks all frol-

---

...any Hot-house or Sweating-house, for Ease and Health of Men, to which be resorting or conversant any Strumpets, or Women of Evil Name or Fame. Or if there be any...for Women, to which is any common recourse of young Men, or other Persons of evil Fame and Suspect Conditions. Also, if there be any such Persons that keep or hold any such Hot-houses, either for Men or Women, and have found no surety to the Chamberlain for their good and honest Behavior, according to the laws of the City, and lodge any manner of person by Night, contrary to the Ordinance thereof made, by the which he or they shall forfeit 20 pounds to the Chamber, if they do the contrary.

— 15th century English Ordinance

---

icked together in the nude. Large galleries, like those found in modern swimming pools, ran around the baths so spectators could ogle the bathers. Floating tables were available for eating and gaming. In a word, the stews were lewd.

An outraged church and state began passing laws against communal bathing which eventually led to the end of the public baths. During the reign of Henry VIII some stews were closed; others were closely regulated for 150 years. In 1538, the French stews were completely demolished by Francis I. The church condemned public bathing as promiscuous, and more laws were passed forbidding the practice, although few were enforced or obeyed. As early as 745 A.D., St. Boniface forbade mixed bathing, calling the public baths *seminaria venenata* (hotbeds of vice). At issue in the church was the morality of mixed bathing, not of bathing in general.

Some members of the clergy recommended bathing, while others opposed it. At the beginning of the Middle Ages, St. Gregory the Great allowed baths on Sundays as long as they were taken only for health and cleanliness. In the 8th century, Pope Adrian I urged the clergy to bathe every Thursday. St. Rigobert had baths specially built for the canons of his church, and even provided the wood to heat them. Most monasteries had *lavatoriums*—stone troughs filled with cold water for washing before and after meals. Baths were used in monastic discipline as rewards and punishments. If a monk displayed the proper godliness, he was allowed the luxury of a warm bath. A tub of ice cold water up to the neck punished the sinner.

On the other hand, St. Benedict preached that bathing should not be permitted by "those that are well, and especially to the young." Among the ascetics of the Middle Ages, dirtiness was next to godliness. St. Agnes is said to have died unwashed at age thirteen, while St. Jerome the Blessed scorned his followers for keeping too clean. St. Catherine of Siena never washed, and St. Francis of Assisi reeked to high heaven from lack of bathing.

A milestone in bath history was reached in the 13th century when the Worshipful Company of Plumbers was formed. The Plumber's Charter made it illegal for uninitiates to use the "art and mystery" of plumbing. Anyone who has ever attempted a do-it-yourself plumbing job will vouch for the fact that the art remains a mystery in modern times.

In Elizabethan England of the 16th century, and later in the elegant French courts, bathing was at a premium. Body odors were masked with heady perfumes and dirt was covered with a thick veneer of paints and powders. Perfumers prospered, while water sellers starved. Queen Elizabeth had only one bathtub, which she seldom used. Samuel Pepys kept a diary for nine years, from 1660 to 1669, but only once did he mention his wife bathing. Even such a prolific writer as Shakespeare was fairly silent

---

**My wife busy in going with her woman to
the hot house to bathe herself, after
her long being within doors in the dirt,
so that she now pretends to a resolution
of being very clean. How long it will hold
I can guess.**

— Samuel Pepys

---

on the subject of baths. These unsanitary centuries of filth and vermin were in stark contrast to the frills and lace then in vogue. Ironically, it was the introduction of linen underwear that decreased the necessity of bathing, offering the body protection against the lint residue of the outer clothing.

During the latter half of the 17th century, bathing enjoyed a renewed popularity unknown in Europe since the demise of the Turkish stews. In 1679, the Duke's Bagnio and Bath opened on Long Acre Street, London. Like the medieval stews, this communal bath was modeled after the *hammams* or sweating houses then common in Turkey and the Middle East. The Duke's Bagnio and Bath was an immediate success, and was quickly followed by other public baths. A path paved with black and white marble led to the entrance. The tiled bagnio was also paved with marble and covered by a huge cupola. Marble basins for washing were set into the walls. Four eight-foot rooms adjoined the bagnio, each of a different temperature and containing a lead tub, six feet long by two feet wide. A large salt water bath was located in a separate

---

I also visited the bagnios where a rich man can sup, bathe and sleep with a fashionable courtesan of which species there are many in London. It makes a magnificent debauch and only costs six guineas.

— Casanova

---

room. The bather lounged or strolled around the steam-filled bath, perspiring freely. After stewing for about an hour he was thoroughly dried by a "rubber" (masseur) using a hair-chamolet glove. The rubbing was followed by a warm bath, gradually made colder.

Privacy, even for "private" bathing, was virtually nonexistent. Lords and ladies of the period often entertained visitors while bathing. Having one's portrait painted in the bath was considered chic. Persons of high rank were known to eliminate in the presence of others and it was not uncommon for audiences to be granted while his highness sat on the throne.

Bathing barely made a splash throughout the 18th century. Attitudes toward nudity had changed and a sense of modesty developed to the point that nakedness was sinful. And water was harmful. Only fish took to water. After all, a human could drown in it. Those few eccentrics who practiced ablution bathed in relative obscurity until the 19th century.

THE BATH MODERNE

Up to the 1850's, the private portable bathtub was found mainly in the bedrooms of wealthy Europeans. Buckingham Palace was a noted exception. When Queen Victoria first sat on the throne in 1837, the elegant palace didn't contain a single bath! An embarrassed Parliament voted a yearly allowance of 5000 pounds for the queen's toilette. Her highness was then able to bathe in hot water, piped to the royal tub in the boudoir.

Across the channel, Napoleon gave bathing a boost when it became known that he had given Josephine a tub as a gift. There were times, however, when he insisted that she not bathe for several days prior to lovemaking, since he found the scent of her musk sexually exciting. Napoleon himself took a very hot bath daily while Wellington preferred a daily cold bath. The Emperor's sister, Pauline, bathed in sweet, creamy milk.

The masses of Paris enjoyed no such luxury. The bourgeois were serviced by street vendors, called *baignoires a domicile,* who rolled through Paris on water carts. They hand-carried water into their customers' apartments until late in the century when they were replaced by plumbing.

In colonial America, the Puritans scorned soap and water as being impure. Bathing was a dirty word: it was injurious to health, promoted nudity and encouraged promiscuity. In some states it was actually illegal to bathe. Laws were passed in Ohio, Pennsylvania and Virginia either banning bathing enirely or limiting the number of baths a person could take. Jail awaited the criminal in Philadelphia who bathed more than once a month. Even the purchase of bathtubs was regulated by law.

There were those among the founding fathers who insisted on periodic bathing, the laws nonwithstanding. Ben Franklin picked up the habit in Europe. He brought back a "slipper bath," a macabre contraption in the shape of a slipper in which the lower half of the bather was submerged in the toe. Franklin also experimented with air baths. Bathing in America finally crossed into respectability when the rich Virginia gentry began lining their wooden wash tubs with metal for bathing.

If you stop to consider the work involved in taking a tub bath in early America—or anywhere else—bathing becomes less of a pleasure and more of a pain. You *needed* a bath by the time you completed all the labor necessary to get it. Wood had to be cut and carried inside for a fire. Water was then drawn from the well or the pump and carried to the kitchen. Next, an oilcloth was spread on the floor to catch splashes. The tub was brought from its storage place and filled with water. After bathing, the water had to be carried outside and emptied. Most Americans endured this ritual about once a month. In the meantime, they partially bathed from a basin or outside at the pump. On the frontier, people bathed in rivers and streams, just as their primeval ancestors had done ages before.

The daily ablution of an infant is not more natural or necessary than to take a fish out of water and cover it with dirt once a day, that it might thrive better in its natural element. Cleanliness is next to godliness, but washing should be only to keep the body clean, and this can be done with less than daily scrubbing the whole surface.

—*Mary Baker Eddy*

The bath truly arrived in American society around the 1850's. In 1851, during Millard Fillmore's presidency, the first fixed bathtub was installed in the White House. George Vanderbilt installed the first bathroom in an American home in his New York residence in 1855. Vanderbilt's bathroom was complete with a wash basin, porcelain tub and the ultimate luxury, a flush toilet. Facilities previously located outside or in the bedroom had come together in one room—perhaps the most significant event in the history of the bath.

Hotels were the first American bathroom innovators. As early as 1829, the Tremont House in Boston had eight bathing rooms, located in the basement. The baths were filled with rainwater, caught in a cistern in the attic. In 1853, the Mount Vernon Hotel in Cape May, New Jersey, offered a bath with hot and cold running water for every bedroom.

A Room with a Bath for a Dollar and a Half
— Statler Hotel, 1908

Although bathing was enjoying a renaissance among those who could afford bathrooms or luxury hotels, the mainstream of America continued to lag behind. Up until the 1880's, five out of six city dwellers had no bathroom. Gradually, innovations in plumbing, such as the invention of the flushing water closet by Thomas Crapper in 1872, and mass production of bathtubs provided a bathroom for most homes and apartments. In the meantime, one bathroom had to serve for several families, or one could bathe at the public baths.

The first public bath and washhouse in America was opened in 1852 by the New York Association for Improving the Condition of the Poor in Mott Street. Over 80,000 bathers and 10,000 washers took to the waters in its first year of operation. The city of Boston was the first municipality to operate a bathing establishment by opening the L Street baths in 1866. Up until 1913, the Board of Bath Commissioners regulated all baths and gymnasiums in Boston. The Turkish bath also surfaced again on the bathing scene in 1863, in, of all places, Brooklyn! It was called "The Hammam," after the Turkish baths of the East. More sprang up in other American cities, some becoming centers of vice like their Turkish counterparts of the Middle Ages.

Prodded by Victorian reformers, the politicians of the time considered the communal baths essential for public health. The state of New York passed legislation in 1895 providing for free public baths in all cities of 50,000 population or more. By law the baths had to have hot and cold water, and must be kept open a minimum of fourteen hours a day. For five cents, one could buy a hot bath, a towel and a cake of soap.

Around the 1860's, in the United States and abroad, water cures came into vogue as doctors prescribed various "hydropathic" treatments for ailments. Bathers were called patients. These pseudo-medical cures included such macabre baths as the Hip Bath, Rain Bath, Wet Sheet Pack, Ascending Douche Bath, Hot Air Bath, Boot Bath and Electric Light Bath. Few of these water cures included soap, however, as it was considered odd to bathe for other than medical reasons.

By the 1870's, the hot water heater was a fairly common fixture in American homes. Often known to explode, it sat perilously in the kitchen and was filled with rainwater from a rooftop cistern. As hot water became more universally available, bathing flourished, although private bathrooms still remained a rich man's reality and a poor man's dream.

Since the first private bathrooms were converted bedrooms, they displayed the lavish trappings of an upper class Victorian boudoir. Bathrooms became status symbols and showcases of affluence. They were large rooms containing oriental rugs, curtains, hand-painted, gilded chests and marble sinks and tubs cased in elegantly carved mahogany. The prim and proper Victorian may have sat on toilet that was a sculpted porcelain Cupid holding a heart with a hole in the middle. Another favorite was a porpoise holding a shell. A footbath, scale and medicine chest were standard equipment. All pipes were discreetly hidden from view in wooden cabinets. Despite the elegance, the bathtub was only used

---

Pour into the bath sufficient water to cover the body of the patient, with the exception of his head, when he lies upon his back. After he has lain in the bath for five minutes, his body should be well rubbed by the hands of a healthy bath attendant, and also by his own. It will add materially to the effects of the bath if the bowels or abdomen be gently, but thoroughly, manipulated and kneaded.

— Directions for the Full Bath

---

about once a week, usually on Saturday night. Sponge baths were taken during the week as daily bathing was still believed harmful.

Boxed-in bathrooms came under heavy attack in the 1890's. Dirt and germs lurked in difficult-to-clean cabinets and hard-to-reach corners. To facilitate proper cleaning and sanitation, the boxes were discarded, the furniture removed, the pipes exposed and the bathroom stripped to its bare essentials.

When the bathroom arrived in middle class America, around the turn of the century, it was a white-tiled, antiseptic-looking chamber, much like a hospital room. Everything was spotlessly clinical, with the dazzling whiteness of polished porcelain and enamel. Even the accessories—towels, washcloths, bath mat—were pure white. The white enameled bathtub grew ball and claw feet to raise it off the unsanitary floor. This stark decor dominated the bathroom until the advent of decorator colors in the 1920's.

By the turn of the century, the bath and the room it came to occupy had evolved more or less to the stage we find it today. The ablution revolution gave the bath to the common man, making the bathroom an integral part of the home. Many homes have two, three or more private bathrooms conveniently located off the bedrooms. Although the American bathroom has shrunk drastically in size, becoming more personalized in the process, the trend seems to be shifting back toward larger, more luxurious rooms. Large or small, the bathroom is one of the last bastions of privacy in an ever-increasing population; a secluded place where you can shut out the world and steep yourself in your own private thoughts, hopes and dreams.

A central feature of the modern, private bathroom is the modern, private bathtub, which itself boasts a colorful and curious history.

RUB-A-DUB-DUB

THE TALE OF THE TUB

Basically, all that is needed
to take a bath
is water and a waterproof container.
Once inside the
container the act of bathing is the same, whether
the tub
is made of wood or marble.

The main purpose of the bathtub is, and always has been, functional. It can also serve a decorative function, depending on the fortunes of the bather. Even though the materials, sizes and shapes of bathtubs have changed from time to time, there is no clean evolutionary progression from an "ancient" to a "modern" tub.

The oldest known bathtub, found at the palace of Minos in Crete, dates back to 1700 B.C. Compare the form of this 3700 year old relic with an 1890's tub and the two are virtually indistinguishable. Today we are probably closer to our ancestors in the bathtub than anywhere else.

Ancient Greek bathers splashed around in polished marble tubs resembling giant bird baths. Later the Roman legions carried their portable copper tubs all over the known world. A Roman's private villa bath was a measure of his wealth. Precious metals and fine marble were used for the tub, silver for the pipes. The ultimate in Roman ingenuity were small bathtubs suspended from the ceiling by ropes where one could soak in swinging liquidity.

Oak and walnut provided the materials for the tubs of the Middle Ages. They were round or oval, and came in large and small sizes. A solo model accomodated one bather, while the large size could hold family and guests simultaneously. Many tubs had a shelf across the middle for food and drink. Every medieval monastery had its portable wooden tub. Kirkstall Abbey in England has the only known fixed tub, sunk deep in the courtyard. This 13th century stone tub was filled from a lead pipe and emptied into a drain with a huge stone plug.

In the medieval palaces the baths were more befitting royalty. The "baynes" at Westminster Palace, in 1275, had fixed, case-in tubs, tiled floors, bath mats and water heating facilities.

Under the French influence in the 17th and 18th centuries, the tub took on grandiose dimensions. Late in the 1700's, Casanova scandalized Paris with a tub built for two. The idea of two tubs—one for washing, the other for rinsing—soon caught on and all of fashionable Paris was taking double baths. This is why the French refer to the bath in the plural *(salle de bains)*. Marie Antoinette bathed daily, but was considered odd because she used only one bathtub.

The most impressive tub of the period, built by Louis XIV, can still be seen at Versailles. This octagon-shaped tub measures ten feet wide, three feet deep, and is made of pink marble. When the king bathed, which wasn't very often, a magnificent draped pavillion encircled the tub. Louis XV presented the tub to Madame Pompadour and it took twenty-two men to move it!

Around this era metal began replacing the heavy, cold marble tubs then in use. Wooden tubs were lined with copper, lead or tin. As bathtubs become status symbols, their decorative function was emphasized. They were designed to occupy the bedrooms as pieces of fine furniture, and were among the most elegant baths known. Some were chair or lounge-type baths, linen-lined, with padded backs and submerged, lace-trimmed draperies. A zinc settee tub of the period was built into an elaborately decorated wooden cabinet. For comfort, it had a padded backrest and leather armrests. A hinged lid, fitted over the bather's head, served as a tray from which to eat or drink. Hammock baths were also quite popular.

After an interval of non-bathing during the Age of Reason, the tub surfaced in the 1850's in a variety of curious forms. Called "Geysers," these infernal machines heated the water by gas. They resembled violin cases, women's hats, boots—just about anything you'd never expect to bathe in. Shower baths also began to appear in the mail order catalogs, rivaling the tubs with their grotesque appearances. Unfortunately, the bather had to provide the power to pump the water to the spout. This was done by hand levers, or, in the case of the Virginia Stool Shower, pedal-operated like a bicycle. Some showers had built-in, rotating scrub brushes, also

hand-operated. For some reason, these early exercise showers never caught on.

The more standard tubs were made of wood-encased sheet metal, with a high-standing, cased-in splash-back. Cast iron replaced sheet metal late in the 19th century. The cast iron tubs were simply designed rectangular basins, painted on the outside, often with marble veining on the inside.

...many copper and tin baths have lately been constructed in London, with a little furnace attached to one end, and surrounded with a case or jacket, into which the water flows and circulates backwards and forwards till the whole mass in the bath gets heated to the due degree.

—Magazine of Science and School of Arts, 1842

With the invention of new methods of mass production and the widespread use of porcelain enamels, the bathtub became standardized at 5½ feet, with roll rims and built-in faucets. This archaic, inadequate, uncomfortable, unsafe and dangerous tub became a familiar object in millions of bathrooms for decades to come. The only significant addition was the shower. At first the shower was attached to the tub; later the pipes were built into the wall of the shower stall. Many of us still bathe in similar tub and shower combinations. Surveys show that in adult households where tub and shower combinations exist, 43% use only the shower and never take a tub bath. Incidentally, the old enameled, cast iron bathtubs with claw feet are bringing high prices as collector's items.

Today, bathtubs come in a deluge of shapes, sizes and designs to fit every pocketbook. Your soaking tub can be a huge sunken pool, encased in stone or lava rock, complete with your own private waterfall. Perhaps you'd prefer a solo silver tub set in mahogany or an elegant tub of carved marble. Large family-style baths for communal bathing are available with several whirlpools and molded seats placed at different water levels. How about two matching tubs, His and Hers?

A Millionaire's Luxury...Like owning a yacht or a country estate — like traveling in a private Pullman — like smoking fifty-cent cigars — the daily enjoyment of a *needle* **shower is something that has always smacked of luxury and wealth.**
— American advertisement, 1916

In 1958 the Cornell University Center for Housing and Environmental Studies began extensive research into the bathroom and the various activities performed there. One of the results of the study was a criteria for the ideal bathtub.

This super-tub is an attractive, one-piece molded unit, contoured to the human body and made of skid proof plastic or fiberglass. It measures 6 feet long, 22 inches wide, 16 inches deep, with a rim width of 2½ inches. A seat is provided for washing. The tub slopes toward the backrest to compensate for the tendency of the body to float away from the back. A water circulation system within the tub was found to be the most ideal for temperature control and rinsing, although such a system is relatively expensive. In lieu of water circulation, a flexible, hand operated shower spout can be substituted. The water passes through a diverter mechanism similar to the common kitchen spout. A single, large, hot and cold water spout fills the tub faster. Controls are lever or throttle type, located at a height of 32 inches. The drain is near the deepest end of the tub — at the opposite end from the water spout — to provide for faster drainage and easier tub cleaning. Grab bars and soap dishes are within easy reach to minimize hazards. A similar tub can be easily installed in your present bathroom and is well worth the cost in terms of safety and comfort.

For the future, look for a bathtub that has its water temperature and sudsing controlled by a computer. Such a tub has already been developed at McMaster University in Canada, and can be installed in your home for between $5000 and $8000. Also be prepared to throw away the hot water heater. In the future, water for bathing and other household uses will be heated by solar energy.

The Cornell study concluded that bathing equipment must be designed for bathing functions, rather than the other way around. Herein lies submerged the moral of the tale of the tub: You filled your tub — now you must lie in it. Why not step out of the Dark Ages and into a modern bathtub that doesn't feel like a liquid straight jacket.

SOAPS AND SUDS

99 44/100% PURE

Coming to grips with the origin of soap is
like groping for a soap sliver
in a tub full of water:
just when you think you have it,
it slips through your fingers.

Legend tells us that soap was discovered in ancient times by pagans who sacrificed animals to the gods by fire. The melted animal fats and wood ashes combined, and, when washed into a nearby river, made the water froth and foam. Women gathered at the river to wash clothes in the magical yellowish suds.

From primitive times, man has used soap substitutes or "natural soaps." These were usually plant substances containing "saponins"—detergent cleansers naturally produced by some plants. Soap plants are common to the Fertile Crescent, the birthplace of the ancient civilizations. American Indians washed with the roots and leaves of yucca, fuschia leaves, agave, and scrubbed with soapwort-leaf washcloths. In South America, Indians still use soapbark and soapberry. Even powdered horse chestnuts have been used for soap. Some of these ancient natural cleansers, like soapwort, are found in modern shampoos, hair lotions and conditioners.

Soapmaking is at least 5000 years old. Sumerian tablets mentioned a crude soap for cleansing as early as 3000 B.C. Another Sumerian tablet, dating to 2200 B.C., gives a soap formula consisting of water, alkali and oil. Around 2800 B.C. the Mesopotamians were making soap by boiling fats and ashes together. A soap made with washing soda and potash is mentioned in The Bible by the prophet Jeremiah, but it was only used for washing clothes. A laundry dating from 79 A.D. has been uncovered in the ruins of Pompeii.

The ancients made personal use of soap as hairdressings, shampoos, mouthwashes, and even as dressings for treating wounds. One of these cosmetics was referred to by Pliny the Elder in the 1st century A.D. He described *sapo*, a preparation made by the Gauls from goat's fat and beech ashes, and used as a bleach for the hair. This soft potash soap was converted into hard soda soap by treating the paste repeatedly with salt. Another soap, mentioned by the Greek philosopher, Theophrastus, was made from root ashes steeped in wine.

Wood ashes, high in alkali content, when mixed with water and natural skin oils, will form soap and produce a cleansing lather. The first mention of using soap to wash the body was made by Galen, a 2nd century Greek physician. He also prescribed soap for the treatment of elephantiasis.

In ancient Egypt, Greece and Rome, when bathing and cosmetics were enjoying their finest hour, soap was practically unknown. Anthony and Cleopatra "washed" with an abrasive mixture of fragrant oils and fine white sand. A similar perfumed clay is still used as a cleanser by primitive Africans.

Years ago disgusting lotions and poisonous compounds were largely used by ladies. But a *new era* dawned upon the *Social World* when the *Rev. A.A. Constantine* returned from his missionary labors in Africa, bringing with him a knowledge of the healing arts of the natives of that country. The result was the introduction of the now *world-renowned Constantine's Persian Healing Pine Tar Soap.*
— *American advertisement, 1894*

It is believed that the Phoenicians were the first to develop soapmaking into an art. The Arabs, Turks, Vikings and Celts all made soap. The Celts brought soapmaking to England about 1000 A.D., from where its use and manufacture spread throughout Europe. By the 9th century, homemade soap was fairly common. Italy, Spain and France were centers of commercial soapmaking by the 13th century. Throughout the Middle Ages, soap was used mainly for laundry while the people washed with perfumed toilet waters. The mysteries of soapmaking were kept secret by "soap-boiling" guilds, whose members were admitted only after a long apprenticeship and at great cost.

Up to the 16th century there was still a reluctance to use soap for washing the body. Like bathing, fine soaps could only be afforded by the rich. In 1712, Cromwell almost taxed cleanliness into oblivion in England. Soap monopolies, combined with heavy taxes and high prices, kept manufactured soap scarce until well into the 19th century. Napoleon paid two francs for a bar of perfumed Brown Windsor, an inflated price for 1808. In 1853, when Gladstone grudgingly repealed the English soap tax, he condemned soap as "most injurious both to the comfort and health of the people."

In early America, soapmaking remained as women's work until late in the 1800's. Grandma made her famous lye soap by boiling leftover fat drippings with wood ashes. She often made a year's supply of soap in one day, usually in the early spring. The first

---

Its [99 44/100%] origin was strictly mathematical and precise. It is the result of an analysis made generations ago by a chemist of national fame and was corroborated by an equally celebrated authority... As for the meaning of 'pure' the statement means that Ivory Soap as far as it is possible analytically to determine by chemical analysis, is 99 44/100% pure...
    —Procter & Gamble, 1932

---

commercial soapmakers purchased fat and ashes from the households, converted it into soap, then sold it back to the people door to door. In 1806, the first plant for rendering fats into tallow opened in New York City. Grocers bought soap in large cakes and

cut pieces to size as desired. Around 1830, individually wrapped bars of uniform weight were being produced in New York. Soap powders and liquid soaps followed, and in 1878 Procter & Gamble introduced the first floating soap, called White Soap. The next year it was renamed Ivory Soap. The slogan "99 44/100% Pure" was added in December, 1882. Lifebuoy introduced an antiseptic soap—and B.O.—in 1895.

Prior to the 1920's, laundry soaps and toilet soaps were very much one and the same. With the advent of greater research and understanding of soap chemistry, the spread of technical literature, and the sophistication of advertising and promotion, countless brands of laundry and toilet soaps became commonplace. From its ancient pagan origin, soap has bubbled into a modern multi-billion dollar industry.

BON SAVON

Few luxuries of modern living are as much taken for granted as soap. No longer a rare curiosity, the numerous shapes, scents, colors and textures of soap are always at hand. If America is not the cleanest nation on earth, it is without a doubt the soapiest.

The great American soap opera is played out daily in millions of homes. Like some magical charm, soap promises more than mere cleanliness. Beauty, love, happiness, wealth and the realization of the American Dream reward the user of the right soap. In the United States, where there's soap, there's hope—and there's a soap for every age, occupation and occasion.

What is this slippery stuff that magically foams away all that is vile, dirty and loathsome? What does it do?

In the jargon of chemistry, soaps are compounds formed by the action of fats and alkalis. In other words, fat plus alkali equals soap. Only natural fats are used in soapmaking—animal tallow, nut oils, unsaturated oils—either alone or in combinations. Castile soap was originally made with pure olive oil, once believed to be the only vegetable oil harmless to the skin. Caustic soda (lye) or caustic potash are used as alkali. Most commercial toilet soaps are made up of about 80% tallow and 20% coconut oil. The oil to alkali ratio is approximately 2 to 1. In the so-called "cold process", the oils and a water-alkali solution are heated separately to the desired temperature, then mixed together. The result of this saponification is a combination of soap and glycerin. After the mixture thickens to its proper consistency, it is poured into molds and allowed to cool. Most commercial soap manufacture does not use the cold process, but uses either variations of the full-bodied process, in which as much as one-half million pounds of soap may be produced in a single batch, or variations of the continuous process. All of these techniques are vastly more sophisticated and complicated than the cold process, and insure better control and less variation in the nature of the final product. In commercial production, the glycerin often is separated from the soap and sold as a profitable side product. Most of our glycerin comes from soapmaking. Other ingredients— perfumes, colors, medications—can be added to the soap base

---

**What a magnificent style of life
soap displays!**
— Francis Ponge, Soap

---

at various stages to produce a multitude of soap products. Although these additives may improve the soap in many ways, they do not necessarily enhance its cleansing property. In fact, coloring and perfumes can be used to mask imperfections.

The price of soap is affected by the quality and origin of its ingredients. Only the purest, least odorous fats and oils are used in fine soapmaking. Expensive perfumes can greatly inflate the price of a soap. Perfumes made with natural essential oils are often present in the most expensive products, while inexpensive scents, usually synthetic, are found in the cheaper soaps. A high quality toilet soap is hard, long-lasting and retains its scent to the last sliver. The lather should be fine and sudsy, leaving the skin satiny soft. Old soap will last longer than new because the water has had more time to evaporate from the bar, leaving it hard. Soap should be bought well in advance and stored unwrapped in a cool, dry place. A poor quality soap may be high in alkali content which dries and irritates the skin. Cheaper oils may also produce a soap which is irritating. Toilet soap should not contain more than 2/10 of 1% free alkali. Inferior soaps may contain fillers such as clays or carbonates, and have a fatty, even rancid odor. In fact, the typical odor of soap is the odor of impurities; not of pure, fine soap.

The ritual of cleanliness is consummated when soap unites with water, resulting in a physical-chemical process (detergency) which suspends bacteria, making it possible to wash them from the skin.

**The sweet perfume of a toilet soap
is not so feeble a decoy as one thinks.**
— Rousseau

Your choice of soap should be based on your personal needs, your finances, and, most important, your skin condition. Some soaps are good for dry skin; others for oily. In certain cases, soap can actually be harmful to the skin. Those with allergies, dermatitis or any other skin problems should consult a doctor for special cleansing preparations.

The best way to understand and appreciate the subtleties of soap is by making it yourself. You can make soap in your own kitchen with many products found at the supermarket. For the more esoteric oils, look in health food stores or pharmacies. Soap manufacturers are the best sources of tallow, or it can be ordered from some butchers. Lard is a good substitute for tallow. Lye can be bought at the supermarket.

KITCHEN SOAPMAKING

At a time when personal pride in self sufficiency and craftsmanship are enjoying a renaissance, kitchen soapmaking has a strong appeal. However, *soapmaking can be hazardous.* Concentrated caustic chemicals such as lye must be used. Without careful handling, lye solutions can be spilled or splashed. Mixtures of hot chemicals, fats and soaps can foam and splatter. Always pour the lye solution outside or near an open window. *Do not breathe the fumes.* The finished product may not be completely reacted soap and therefore high in free alkali content. There are no facilities in the kitchen for testing homemade soap, except on yourself, and this you must do at your own risk. Follow the instructions carefully, paying particular attention to measurements and temperatures. Ye shall see marvels!

EQUIPMENT NEEDED
· scale, with measurements to the ½ ounce
· 4 quart glass, enamel or stainless steel pot (for fats)
· heavy glass bottle, with lid (for lye solution). Punch 2 holes in lid for pouring, about 1/8 inch in diameter.
· wooden spoon
· 2 soap or stainless steel meat thermometers
· basin of cold water, large enough to hold soapmaking pot
· basin of warm water, large enough to hold lye bottle
· cardboard box, with lid
· heavy plastic wrap
· rubber gloves and apron

RENDERING FATS
Waste kitchen fats can be used in soapmaking. Store grease drippings and fat trimmings, preferably beef, in the refrigerator. To

render, place fats in a pot, cover with water, and melt over low heat. Strain melted fat through one layer of nylon stocking. Retain strained fat and throw away residue. Store fat in refrigerator until solid. When ready to make soap, remove tallow and discard the water that has settled on the bottom. Very rancid or odorous fats should be rendered twice in the same manner.

DIRECTIONS FOR SOAPMAKING

Preparing the Ingredients
1. Place lye bottle on scale and note weight. Add required weight of lye. *All measurements given, including liquids, are by weight.*
2. Add required weight of *cold* water to lye and stir with wooden spoon handle. The temperature will rise to about 180 degrees. *Be sure to wear rubber gloves and apron throughout the soapmaking process.* Set lye solution aside to cool. Rinse spoon.
3. Weigh fats and place in soapmaking pot. Melt over very low heat until all fats are dissolved. Remove pot from heat and place in basin of cold water. The temperature will begin to drop. Immerse one thermometer in fats for reading.
4. Place *cooled* lye solution in basin of warm water. The temperature will begin to rise. Place thermometer in solution for reading.
5. When both the fat and lye solution have reached the desired temperatures, the two are ready to mix. Cap lye bottle *tightly* before pouring solution.

Mixing the Soap
6. Set fats into motion by stirring in a steady, circular pattern with a wooden spoon. *Do not stir too rapidly.* Keep fats in motion while pouring lye.
7. Pour lye into fats in a slow, steady stream.
8. Continue stirring until mixture thickens to the consistency of

honey (about 30 to 45 minutes). If after stirring for 45 minutes the mixture does not thicken, place pot in cold water and continue stirring until proper consistency is reached.

Pouring the Soap

9. Pour thickened soap mixture into a cardboard box that has been lined with plastic wrap. Box size depends on the amount of soap made and the shape of cake desired. Special soap molds can also be used, in which case they should be lightly oiled with *mineral oil* before filling.
10. Place lid on box and store wrapped in a blanket for 24 hours.
11. Unmold and let the cake age at least two weeks in the open air before cutting into bars. If an outer layer of soda ash has formed on the cake, trim it off before using.

BASIC SOAP RECIPE
(Makes 2.3 pounds)

4 oz. lye
10 oz. water
_____

24 oz. tallow

lye temperature: 85° to 95° F.
fat temperature: 120° to 130° F.

VEGETABLE OIL SOAP

Several vegetable oils may be substituted for tallow in the Basic Soap Recipe, either alone or in combinations. Vegetable oil soaps will be softer than tallow or lard soaps. Mineral oil will not make soap. Following is a list of usable vegetable oils:

- castor oil
- coconut oil
- cottonseed oil
- hydrogenated vegetable shortening
- linseed oil
- palm oil
- peanut oil
- soybean oil

PURE VEGETABLE SOAP
(Makes 2.2 pounds)

4 oz. lye
9½ oz. water
_____

16 oz. Crisco
7 oz. olive oil

lye temperature: 70° to 75° F.
fat temperature: 80° to 85° F.

SCENTED SOAP

Essential oils are the best for scenting soap. The oils may be used alone or in fragrant blends. Add oil before pouring soap into mold and stir in thoroughly. For a light scent, add ¼ *fluid* oz. oil per 2 lbs. soap; for stronger scent, add ½ *fluid* oz. oil per 2 lbs. soap.

SPICY CARNATION SOAP
(Makes 2.2 pounds)

4 oz. lye
9½ oz. water

16 oz. lard
7 oz. coconut oil
¼ oz. essential carnation oil

lye temperature: 70° to 75° F.
fat temperature: 80° to 85° F.

SOAP POTPOURRI

ALMOND SOAP
A quality white curd soap perfumed with sweet almond oil, oil of bitter almond, or benzaldehyde (artificial almond essence). Inferior products may contain nitrobenzole, a synthetic bitter almond-type fragrance.

CASTILE SOAP
A mild soap originally made with pure olive oil. Today many "Castile" soaps are made with other vegetable oils. Top quality Castile soap is white, while the inferior grade is yellow. Castile is a marvelous cleanser, producing a rich lather.

CREAM SOAPS
Soaps containing cold cream materials, moisturizers and emollients. Cream soaps are particularly good for dry and delicate skin.

DEODORANT SOAPS
Soaps to which antibacterial agents have been added to reduce odor-causing bacteria. Deodorant soaps are not recommended for sensitive skin. As with all soaps, they should be thoroughly rinsed from the skin. Good for normal and oily skin.

DETERGENT SOAPS
Synthetic non-soap cleansing products made with mild detergent sudsers and often containing emollients. Foam well in hard water. Detergent soaps eliminate most scum and bathtub ring. Good for normal and oily skin. Combination soaps are a mixture of soap and mild detergents.

FLOATING SOAPS
Unmilled soaps with a high moisture content. Air is incorporated into the mixture, causing the bar to float. Floating soaps do not keep well due to high loss of moisture and scent. Lather freely.

GELEES
Liquid soaps or detergents used for bathing or as shampoos. Some gels contain herbs, proteins and moisture balancers. Bath gelées can be poured under the running water like bubble bath or used with a sponge or washcloth.

GERMICIDE SOAPS
Soaps containing antiseptic ingredients used for cleansing wounds and for surgical cleansing. Not recommended for daily use or bathing unless prescribed by a doctor.

HARD WATER SOAPS
Soaps containing water softeners. Hard water soaps should not be used on the face, or by people with dry or delicate skin.

HANDMADE OR MULTI-MILLED SOAPS
Expensive soaps of fine texture, scent and color. Sometimes called French soaps, these bars are low in alkali and moisture content. Multi-milling insures quality throughout the life of the bar.

HYPO-ALLERGENIC SOAPS
Mild formula soaps, low in potential irritants, especially designed for allergic skin. Hypo-allergenic soaps usually produce a poor lather.

MEDICATED SOAPS
Soaps containing medications such as tar, sulphur, or antibacterial ingredients, used to treat acne and other skin disorders. Medicated

soaps require thorough rinsing. Not recommended for sensitive skin.

MILK SOAPS
Soaps containing milk or milk by-products. Milk soap is rich in protein and is often recommended for delicate skin and complexion care. Proteins may be irritating to sensitive skin.

MILLED SOAPS
These are the most commonly used, mass produced soaps. The quality is usually good. Milling refers to the mixing of color, perfume and soap flakes. Milled soaps are only milled once, whereas multi-milled soaps are milled several times to reduce water content and produce a hard, uniform bar.

OATMEAL SOAP
A rough-textured soap to which oatmeal has been added. The oatmeal acts as a mild abrasive and latherer. Good for oily, dry and normal skin.

SALT WATER SOAP
Often a coconut or other vegetable oil soap with low tallow content. May contain foam builders and water softeners. May also be a non-soap detergent "soap". Can be used in hard water. Salt water soap can be irritating to the skin because of the coconut or vegetable oil content.

SAND SOAP
An abrasive soap containing fine siliceous sand, Calais sand, sea sand or powdered pumice stone. Sand soaps are usually crude, hard soaps designed for heavy cleansing and are not suitable for regular use or for the face.

SOAPLESS SOAPS
Cleansers for people who are soap sensitive and cannot use regular soaps. Excellent for dry and sensitive skin as they do not leave a soap residue. These mild detergent products may also be used in hard or salt water.

SOAP POWDER OR CHIPS
Dried soap blended with a high amount of builders and extenders and relatively high water content. May contain as little as 20% soap.

SUPERFATTED SOAPS
Soaps containing extra fat or oil, such as lanolin, cocoa butter, coconut oil, petrolatum or tallow. Lubricate and smooth dry and sensitive skin. Superfatted soaps also help the skin retain its natural moisture due to their high fat content.

TRANSPARENT OR GLYCERIN SOAPS
Expensive soaps traditionally made by an involved process of heating good quality soap with alcohol, then distilling off about 80% of the alcohol. The result is a translucent bar with a low alkali content. Although a poor latherer, it leaves the skin with a soft emollient feeling. Requires thorough rinsing.

WASHBALLS OR SAVONETTES
Round soaps made from good toilet soap stock. They are formed by pressing the soap into molds or are shaped by hand.

CLEANLINESS IS NEXT TO GODLINESS

SKIN DEEP

Cleanliness, says the sage,
is next to godliness.
On a more earthly plane, cleanliness is essential to
our personal, social and hygenic well-being.
In heaven and earth,
cleanliness is truly an immaculate concept.

To be clean is to be comfortable in both mind and body. You can live with yourself, and, in a crowded society, you can live with others. You emerge from the tub a new person, squeaking clean and impeccably decent, with a euphoric glow that only soap and water can produce. In a very real sense, you are reborn of the water. You have, so to speak, stepped into a new skin.

The skin serves four basic functions: sensory, excretory, heat-regulating and respiratory. The latter two functions are most affected by bathing. In addition, bathing is also important to peripheral circulation in those tiny veins and capillaries close to the surface of the skin.

Skin is made up of several complex layers. The topmost layer, which contains our pigment cells, is called the epidermis. Skin has its own life and death cycle. The entire skin surface is shed every 28 days, to be replaced by new, healthy tissue. Old, dead skin must be removed frequently by washing to avoid clogging the sebaceous and sweat glands. This decaying skin, combined with dirt in the environment, clothing residue, natural body oils and perspiration, can inhibit the skin's respiratory function. There are as many bacteria on your skin as there are people on the earth. Up to two million bacteria reside snugly in your armpit! Some of these microorganisms are harmless; others are even useful and play an active role in keeping the skin healthy. As these bacteria lie on the skin's surface, certain chemical processes take place resulting in body odors. Water cleanses, detoxifies and deodorizes the skin. The skin requires water to remain healthy, elastic and supple. Without water, skin becomes dehydrated and begins to crack and scale.

In order to determine which method of bathing or which cosmetics are best for you, you must first determine the condition of your skin. Dry skin feels rough and sensitive, and is prone to redness and chapping. Over-bathing can be harmful to dry skin. Showers have a lesser drying effect than baths. Older people

frequently suffer from dry skin because as skin ages it produces less natural oil. The skin of infants also produces little oil, so babies should be given an occasional oil bath. If you have dry skin, use super-fatted soaps and a bath oil. An afterbath oil or moisturizing skin cream should also be applied after bathing. Pay special attention to exposed areas such as hands, elbows, legs and knees.

Beauty commonly produces love; but cleanliness preserves it.
— Joseph Addison

Oily skin will appear shiny and leave a greasy stain when wiped with a clean, white tissue. It is associated with clogged pores and blackheads and requires frequent cleansing. When bathing, thoroughly wash the hairy parts of the body, especially the hair on the head. More oil is secreted on the head, more dirt accumulates there, and it is less frequently washed than the rest of the body.

Normal skin is smooth, supple and translucent. If you are blessed with normal skin, thank your lucky stars—and keep it clean!

Always use a fresh, clean washcloth each time you bathe. Rinsing is very important after bathing to wash away all traces of soap. Soap residue left on the skin can cause serious irritation. Be sure to dry thoroughly. A brisk rubdown with a terrycloth towel stimulates circulation in the skin, leaving you with a healthy glow.

HOT AND COLD RUNNING WATER

Water temperatures affect the body in various ways—some beneficial, some harmful. *Always exercise caution when bathing in extreme hot or cold water.* Overexposure to extremes of temperature constitutes the greatest danger in bathing. It is wise to use a bath thermometer. They are inexpensive, easy to read, and may save you a lot of misery.

Be sure to dry thoroughly when emerging from your bath. To avoid catching colds, pay special attention to drying the damp hair at the nape of the neck.

An average bath uses 30 gallons of water. A shower uses about three gallons per minute.

HOT BATHS (98 to 112 Degrees F.)

Hot baths are extremely enervating and should not be taken for more than 20 minutes. Gradually add hot water to a warm bath. *Do not* plunge into hot water. Remember that a hot bath is just as stimulating as a cold bath. Breathing becomes shallow and the heartbeat quickens. In a hot bath, your heartbeat can increase up to four times the normal rate in order to pump blood to heat-dilated vessels. Obese people or those with heart trouble *should not* take hot baths. *Do not* put hot water on your face as it can rupture the tiny capillaries near the skin surface. After a few minutes in a hot bath the muscles relax and breathing becomes normal, although oxygen intake remains relatively low.

Massaging sore muscles in a hot bath will usually bring immediate relief. Hot baths are used in the treatment of several ailments, including gout, neuritis, arthritis, sciatica, bronchitis, abdominal colic and muscular spasms. Baths *will not* cure these ailments, but they can relieve pain. *Do not* attempt to treat yourself without the advice of a physician.

The hotter the water, the more moisture the body loses and the drier the skin becomes. People with dry skin *should not* take hot baths. The hot, slow bath also eliminates body toxins. In water over 100 degrees F., as much as two quarts of perspiration—equaling four pounds—can be eliminated in 30 minutes. *Do not* attempt to reduce in a hot bath as the weight loss is only temporary. The body will replace the lost fluids in a matter of hours. In a very hot bath (104 degrees F.), internal body temperature can rise to as high as 103 to 105 degrees. A danger point is reached when the internal temperature goes above 102 degrees.

**Water is the most healing of all remedies,
and the best of all cosmetics.**
—Arab proverb

A hot bath should be followed by a cool (not cold) rinse to bring the body temperature back to normal. The same result can be achieved with a rub of alcohol or an alcohol-based fluid such as witch hazel or cologne.

WARM BATHS (90 to 98 Degrees F.)

Most of us take warm baths because they are the most comfortable and the best for cleansing. A leisurely soak in a warm tub is one of the supreme pleasures in the human experience.

When taking a warm bath, the temperature should be maintained at a constant 98 degrees for maximum comfort. Warm baths have traditionally been prescribed for nervous tension and insomnia. The soothing, relaxing feeling of a warm bath comes about because the entire body is immersed in a constant or slowly fluctuating temperature approximating the body's normal temperature.

The action of the kidneys can be heightened 50% or more by drinking small quantities of cold water during a warm bath. This increased kidney function helps detoxify the body by eliminating noxious fluids.

Which two would you hire? experienced and intelligent — experienced and intelligent — experienced, intelligent and CLEAN — experienced — intelligent and CLEAN — experienced and intelligent?
— Cleanliness Institute, 1929

COLD BATHS (Under 75 Degrees F.)

Cold baths, like any extreme water temperatures, can be dangerous. After exercise, they can be deadly. The drastic shock of the temperature change causes the body to rapidly give off heat and energy. Circulatory changes occur within 20 seconds, and have been compared to accelerating a car to 40 miles an hour, and then shifting into reverse. This rapid constriction of the blood vessels can actually cause pain. Cold baths *should always* be worked up to gradually, and *should not* be taken for more than three or four minutes at a time. They are the least desirable for cleansing as soap does not lather well in cold temperatures.

Cold water constricts blood vessels and pores with a resulting rise in blood pressure. Paradoxically, a *hot* feeling ensues, much the same as in freezing to death. Underweight people, the constitutionally rundown, the elderly, and people with high blood pressure *should not* take cold baths. Cold baths are excellent for reducing swelling, although this should not be attempted without medical advice.

A cold bath should be followed by a few minutes of vigorous exercise to bring the body temperature back to normal.

BEAUTY AND THE BATH

COSMETICS THROUGH THE AGES

From Cleopatra to Helena Rubenstein,
beauty and the bath have waded hand in hand down the
stream of time.
The natural desire to beautify oneself,
to envelop the body
in a protective coating of fragrant creams, lotions
and oils,
is as old as the art of bathing.

In Egypt, aromatic oils, unguents and balsams were used for offerings to the gods, embalming the dead, cosmetics and bath additives. Cosmetics unearthed in Egyptian tombs are estimated to be between 5500 and 7000 years old. Perfumes guarded the soul on its journey to the hereafter. Cosmetics were made by the priests, the ancient counterparts of the modern cosmetologists. A fine toilet was the pride of every wealthy Egyptian. Scented sesame, almond, castor, olive oils and camel fat were rubbed on the body or added to the bath water. A daily bath, lasting for several hours, was enjoyed by the nobility. Slaves were needed to prepare the bath, scent and heat the water, lay out towels, and massage and anoint the bather with precious oils. Soap, surely the finest cosmetic, was unknown to the Egyptians, who washed with a soda substance or a preparation of fine-grained sand mixed with oil. Even today, soap is not considered a cosmetic under the Food and Drug Act.

The exotic scents of India also waft through the early annals of the cosmetic arts. India abounds in sweet, fragrant flora. Scents from flowers, woods and animals were extracted and mixed with sesame oil to be used for religious offerings and personal beauty. Many cosmetic and bathing customs are revealed in the sacred writings of India and the Middle East. The *Kama Sutra* lays down rules for bathing, shaving and anointing the body with oil. The *Koran* mentions darkening the eyes, and the hymns of Veda proclaim that god should be honored with perfumes.

Cosmetics were introduced to Greece and the Mediterranean by the Phoenicians. By Homer's time there were over 100 cosmetic preparations to choose from. Grecian bodies were perfumed with richly scented almond and olive oils. Some early organic cosmetics contained such bizarre ingredients as ant's eggs, swan's fat and crocodile testicles, all believed to be natural beautifiers. Personal hygiene was so esteemed that the women of Athens could be fined if they were careless in their dress or toilet.

From Greece and Egypt, cosmetics were brought to Rome and incorporated into the lavish Roman bathing rituals. The more the Romans bathed, the more cosmetics they used. Roman men rivaled the women in the use of cosmetics. During the reign of Nero, luxury was the motto of the court. One of the many pleasures of his wife, Poppaea, was to squish around in a marble tub filled with fresh, macerated strawberries. When strawberries were out of season, she bathed in asses' milk. When Poppaea was banished from Rome, she took with her a train of 50 she asses to provide the precious milk for her baths. Perhaps she took her cue from the Arabs, who believed that bathing in asses' milk promoted sexual vigor. Nobles often traveled with special carriages containing cosmetics, scents, several bath attendants, perfumers and barbers. Costly fragrances were stored in elegant ivory boxes. The poor used inferior scents, packed in shells or clay containers. All patrician matrons had an *ornatrix,* a personal maid of the toilet. She was overseer of the slaves and mistress of the *cosmetae* (cosmetics). Juvenal, the Roman poet, enjoyed satirizing these wealthy ladies, who, finding the temperature of their bath water incorrect or the hue of their paint off color, would fling heavy objects, kick, and even prick their slave with a sharp pin. The use of cosmetics, like bathing, declined after the fall of Rome.

By the 12th century, fair maidens all over Europe were being presented with exotic eastern cosmetics brought by knights returning from the Crusades. Rose petals floated on a knight's bath water, and after bathing he was sprinkled with rose water in the Arabian manner. Later in the Middle Ages, cosmetics and communal Turkish baths were condemned by church and state. Women who continued to wear makeup were called "bedizened whores". Proper ladies refused to bathe or use cosmetics until the dawn of the Renaissance.

While the beauty parade was starting in Florence, Anne Boleyn in England was falling out of favor with Henry VIII, partly because

she allowed men to dip into her bath water with their goblets to drink to her health. Anne's daughter, Queen Elizabeth, followed her infrequent hot baths with a wine facial rinse for a blushing complexion. Elizabeth's cousin, Mary, Queen of Scots, recommended that the matrons of her court bathe in wine, the maidens in milk. Elizabethan courtiers stored their cosmetics in large, ornate boxes which also served as bedroom furniture. Smaller cosmetic containers were beautifully decorated with gold and silver inlays or elaborately painted scenes.

That all women, of whatever age, rank, profession, or degree, whether virgins, maids, or widows, that shall, from and after such Act, impose upon, seduce, and betray into matrimony, any of his Majesty's subjects, by the scents, paints, cosmetic washes, artificial teeth, false hair, Spanish wool, iron stays, hoops, high-heeled shoes, bolstered hips, shall incur the penalty of the law in force against witchcraft and like misdemeanours and that the marriage, upon conviction, shall stand null and void.
— *Proposed Act of English Parliament, 1770*

Catherine de Medici brought her Italian beauty secrets to France in the 16th century. Powders, patches and paints were the rage of her court. In the middle 1500's, Maistre Alexys le Piedmontais wrote the earliest known French perfumery book. In it he insisted that one can be beautiful forever by feeding a young raven hard eggs for forty days, killing it, and then distilling it with myrtle leaves, almond oil and talc. This "natural" preparation was then used as a beauty cream. Ever since le Piedmontais, the French have been fashion leaders in the cosmetic arts.

In the 18th century, such notable French beauties as Mesdames

Pompadour, du Barry and de Maintenon led the cosmetic craze. Pompadour alone spent 500,000 francs a year on perfume. There was a brief period in France, during the reign of Louis XIV, when artificial beauty was frowned upon by the king. His objection was short lived, however, and soon the cry of *"vive le poudre à la Maréchale!"* (Long live the beauty box!) was heard again. In 1770, the English Parliament considered beauty aids to be feminine trickery and tried to pass a bill banning them. Fortunately, the bill never passed. Louis XV's court at Versailles, where a new scent was worn every day, was called *la cour parfumée.*

European gentlemen continued to wear make-up until around 1850. Napoleon's quarterly cosmetic bill for 1806 listed 26 jars of almond cream, 162 bottles of cologne and 20 superfine bath sponges. It was during Napoleon's time that the French began using scientific concepts in manufacturing cosmetics.

America was slow to jump on the beauty bandwagon. Even the Southern belles shunned cosmetics in favor of the natural look. When Dolly Madison became the first lady, her charm, sophistication and use of cosmetics gave beauty preparations a fresh air of respectability. Finer cosmetics had to be imported from Europe, as there were no manufacturers in the United States. American women became kitchen cosmetologists, turning out scores of homemade preparations. Painted ladies were still thought vulgar in some Victorian quarters where non-adornment was the rule. Stage star Cora Perl shocked polite society when her press agent revealed that she regularly bathed in champagne.

Flappers made cosmetics a national rage in the Roaring 20's. It was an era of bathtub gin, bubble baths and Betty Boop eyes. Lipsticks, eyebrow pencils, creams and lotions poured out in a steady stream like bootleg champagne. Cosmetic manufacturers proliferated and the cosmetic boom was on. At that time, many products were inferior or harmful. In 1938, the government passed the Food, Drug and Cosmetic Act for consumer protection.

Today cosmetics are a 7 billion dollar industry enjoying a 10% annual growth rate. Bath preparations alone account for an annual sale of $258 million. Men and women everywhere are looking for a little magic in a bottle. Thousands of products claim to fill in where Mother Nature left off. Cosmetics and their claims have recently come under fire from doctors, researchers, consumer groups and Congress, who want to know *exactly* what ingredients are contained in cosmetic preparations.

While the battle of the cosmetic bottle rages, one age old question still remains: Do they work? There is only one place to find the answer. Ask the mirror on the wall.

HOW TO TAKE A BEAUTY BATH

Water is one of nature's best beautifiers. In addition to your daily bath or shower, a 20 minute beauty bath once or twice a week is a necessity for healthier, younger looking skin. A beauty bath will not only pamper the outer you, but the inner you as well.

Any beauty bath worth its salt should be planned in advance. Pick a time when you can relax completely, free from interruptions or pressing engagements. A morning beauty bath is a perfect way to greet the day. An evening bath will leave you drowsy and ready for sleep. Carefully lay out all the toilet articles you will need— additives, lotions, creams, manicuring tools, etcetera. All cosmetics should be removed before bathing. For soft, supple skin, rub cream thoroughly into rough spots—heels, elbows, calloused areas— and leave it on during the bath.

We recommend showering first, giving your entire body a thorough soaping and rinsing. Be sure to use a superfatted soap if your skin is dry. A good long-handled brush or loofah is essential for scrubbing the back between the shoulders.

Now draw a warm bath and add your favorite perfumed additive, making sure it is completely dissolved before entering the tub. A rich bath oil will caress your body and float away flaky, scaly skin. Try blanketing yourself in bubbles one week: a milk bath the next. Bubbles explode with fragrances and act as insulation to keep the water—and you—warm and cozy. Milk products are excellent natural sources of protein-rich bath additives.

A 20 minute soak in warm water will relieve tired muscles, soothe joints and wash away minor aches and kinks. While soaking you can listen to music, read that article you've been putting off, exercise, or simply lie back on your bath pillow and relax. You can also set your hair, apply a face masque, or cream your face, letting the steam enhance the moisturizing process. Soak cotton balls in witch hazel and place on eyelids to relax your eyes along with your body.

After soaking for a few minutes, scrub away any dead skin with a brush or loofah. Use a pumice stone for elbows and feet, and a nail brush for the hands. The bath is the best place to manicure cuticles as they are easier to remove after soaking in warm water. A quick, cool rinse is a refreshing climax to your beauty bath.

Dry by rubbing briskly with a terrycloth towel. Rubbing promotes circulation and leaves you tingling all over and in the pink. Finish up with an after-bath splash of your favorite cologne or dust yourself with some scented powder. For tingling refreshment, put cologne in the freezer for about 15 minutes before using. If you have dry skin, massage with a rich cream lotion.

**There's no place like a bath
to stretch your soul and listen
to your own inner voice.**
            — Seneca

Now take a good long look at yourself in the mirror. Do you recognize that radiant beauty beaming back at you?

BATH BOUTIQUE

AFTER BATH FRESHENERS
Tingling, scented waters, usually high in alcohol content, but occasionally non-alcoholic, which help close pores after bathing. Not recommended for dry or sensitive skin.

BATH OILS
Scented bath oils are available in several forms: foaming, fragrant and moisturizing. The so-called foaming bath oils are often bubble baths under a different name in which the "oil" is the fragrant oil of the bubble bath. Fragrant bath oils are usually non-foaming or low foaming products with a high content of fragrance blended with oils and other materials. Although oils are used mainly to provide luxurious scent to the bath, they may also contain moisturizers. The moisturizing bath oils may be added to the bath, or rubbed on the skin prior to bathing or showering. Most oils can also be smoothed on the skin after the bath. Moisturizing bath oils replace natural oils washed away during bathing. Bath oils often contain vegetable oils—safflower, cottonseed or corn oil—blended with other moisturizers such as lanolins and silicones, which are ideal for dry skin.

BATH SOAKS
These bubbly detergents foam when added to the bath water. They are usually inexpensive products designed for children. Bath soaks are essentially the same as bubble baths.

BOTANICAL BATHS
Dry or liquid vegetable, fruit and herbal products that bring a garden of earthly delights to your tub. Botanical baths are available in a variety of flavors and scents ranging from allspice to water-

melon. Scents can be either natural or synthetic.

BUBBLE BATH
Available in powder, tablet, bead, crystal or liquid forms. Bubble bath scents and foams; some contain oils and water softeners. Bubbles act as insulation to keep the water warm, and help prevent bathtub ring.

COLD CREAM
An emulsified cleansing oil, excellent for restoring moisture lost from the drying effect of free alkali soaps. Cold creams containing lanolin are especially beneficial for dry skin.

CRYSTALS AND SALTS
Crystals and salts add color and fragrance to the bath and act as water softeners. Salts containing a high percentage of alkali may irritate sensitive skin. Although some products contain oil, it is usually not in sufficient quantity to effectively lubricate dry skin. Bath tablets are compressed crystals. As with many bath products and cosmetics, the cost of the packaging can greatly affect the price.

GELS
Gels are smooth-textured, lightly scented, non-soap liquid cleansers. Some gels are available with moisturizers and emollients. Due to their rich lathering properties, gels make fine hair shampoos. Gels produce abundant lather in hard or soft water.

MILK BATHS
Dry or liquid milk products that give you a tub full of creamy fluff. The better milk baths produce a light, airy foam and milky scent. Many buttermilk baths contain lactic acid, a substance reputed to kill harmful bacteria on the skin.

MOISTURIZERS

Moisturizers are beneficial skin softeners and toners. Some moisturizers tend to be greasy and sticky. This is often considered an indication of richness, quality and effectiveness. It is not necessary to suffer discomfort in order to enjoy the softening and protective benefits of moisturizers. Good moisturizers can provide smooth skin without leaving a greasy or sticky residue.

SEA BATHS

Bath products containing seaweed, algae, sea salts, minerals and other marine ingredients. Many foam and color, bringing salty sea scents to your tub. Sea baths come in liquid, powder and tablets.

TALCUM POWDERS

Used mainly for skin irritation, talcum powders absorb excess moisture, protect and lubricate skin. The better powders are finely sieved for maximum absorbency. Many talcs contain deodorant and scent.

TOWELETTES

Small, individually wrapped towels, usually scented, made with an oil moisturizing base. When traveling, perfect for rubbing on your body after a bath or shower. Towelettes may also be used to take a mini-bath when no tub or shower is available.

BATHING AU NATUREL

Ever since the Egyptians first sprinkled rose petals in the bath water, man has been trying to bring nature to the tub. Nature has generously provided many botanicals to turn your bath into a fresh natural environment—an English country garden, a sun-kissed lemon grove, a pine-scented forest.

Botanicals include any vegetable matter or extract, such as herbs, flowers, vegetables, fruits and meals, which can safely be added to the bath. They often serve both aesthetic and therapeutic purposes. A rose bath, for example, fills your bathroom with the delicate fragrance of a rose garden and at the same time is reputed to destroy harmful bacteria on your skin. Lemon and strawberry are good for oily skin, tomato for dry, and orange for normal. Some botanicals, like cucumber, act as astringents, tightening pores. Others, such as allspice, are diaphoretics, opening pores to allow free elimination of body wastes. Jasmine and bergamot are soothing and relaxing; rosemary and spearmint stimulating and invigorating. Elder flowers are natural water softeners. Tea tans the skin beautifully and is a traditional treatment for sunburn. A little lovage added to the bath will make one more loveable.

Meal, such as oatmeal, bran or almond meal, contains oils beneficial to skin tone, as well as being effective cleansers. Meal baths help relieve chapped or scaly skin that has become irritated due to overexposure to sun, wind or cold. The effect of a meal or botanical bath is heightened by following a 20 minute soak with a cool, three minute shower rinse.

A large selection of natural bath additives and cosmetics are available at your bath boutique. You can also compound bath brews and cosmetics in your own kitchen, using many ingredients found at the supermarket or in your own backyard. Kitchen compounding is like cooking, and the result, like a sumptuous meal, is completely satisfying to body and spirit. At this point we leave the bathroom for the kitchen and an introduction to the fascinating art of bathing *au naturel.*

Thy baths shall be the juice of July flowers,
Spirit of roses and of violets,
The milk of unicorns, and panthers' breath
Gathered in bags, and mixed with wines.
— *Ben Jonson*

METHODS

In earlier times, botanicals were steeped in wine and this delicious liquor added to the bath water. This method can still be used, although there are several other ways to introduce botanicals into your bath. In any of these three methods, a few drops of essential oil can be added for a stronger scent.

Direct Method

Sprinkle your favorite herbs or flower petals into the tub before turning on the hot water. Be sure to remove the residue before draining the tub. Fruits and vegetables can be liquified in a blender and strained directly into the warm bath water. Another direct method is to gently simmer botanicals in one cup of water, in a glass container, for 15 to 20 minutes. Heating releases the botanicals' natural essences. Strain mixture into warm water.

Steep Method

Steep botanicals overnight in a cup of white vinegar (or wine), then strain mixture into the tub before filling. The vinegar helps maintain the skin's acid mantle. Or, you can combine equal parts of borax crystals and botanicals in a sealed glass jar and let stand for two weeks before using. Three tablespoons of this water-softening mixture is all that is needed for a fragrant bath.

Bath Bag Method

The most convenient way to add a *bouquet garni* to your tub is with a bath bag. Bath bags can be easily made out of muslin, doubled cheesecloth, old stockings or superfine net. Squeeze the bag several times to release the ingredients. When you enter the tub, swish the bag around in the water and rub it over your body. Soap chips can be added to the bag for sudsing. You can also attach the bag to the bath spout or shower head so the water will run through. Meals can be powdered for bath bags in a blender.

HERBAL BATHS

HERBS AND FLOWERS

Makes 1 Bath

2 tablespoons dried rose petals
1 tablespoon dried lavender flowers
1 tablespoon grated orange peel   1 teaspoon rosemary
1 tablespoon grated lemon peel   2 bay leaves, crushed

Place all ingredients in bath bag. Put bag in tub while water is running. Relax for 20 minutes in this sweet-scented bouquet.

GARDEN OF ALLAH

Makes 1 Bath

4 allspice, crushed   ¼ teaspoon ground cinnamon
4 cardamon seeds, crushed   ½ teaspoon ground ginger
¼ teaspoon ground cloves   2 teaspoons rosemary

Place all ingredients in bath bag. Soak bag in tub while water is running for a bath as exotic as a Persian garden.

SAVORY BATH BAG

Makes 1 Bath

2 tablespoons dried rosemary
2 tablespoons dried thyme   8 fresh mint leaves

Crush all ingredients and place in bath bag. Let bag soak in tub while water is running. Massage your body with this bag full of nature's herbs.

MILK BATHS

SWEET CLOVER MILK BATH

Makes 1 Bath

1 cup powdered skim milk
½ cup oatmeal
10 drops oil of sweet clover

Place milk and oatmeal in bath bag. Immerse bag in water while tap is running. Pour in oil and swish bag around for a country fresh fragrance.

CHOCOLATE MILK BATH

Makes 1 Bath

2 cups fresh milk
2 tablespoons sesame oil
10 drops chocolate oil

Shake all ingredients well and pour under full force of running water. Like bathing in a chocolate milk shake!

BUTTERMILK BATH

Makes 1 Bath

1 cup buttermilk   2 tablespoons wheat germ oil
3 tablespoons Epsom salts   10 drops lemon oil

Mix ingredients well and pour into bath water. Nourishes the skin and fights dryness.

WINE BATHS

CHAMPAGNE AND STRAWBERRIES

Makes 1 Bath

½ cup fresh strawberries   1 teaspoon borax
½ cup powdered oatmeal   10 drops strawberry oil
2 cups champagne

Mash strawberries and mix with oatmeal, borax and oil. Place in bath bag and immerse in water. Pour in one cup champagne. Pour the other cup for yourself.

SUMMER WINE BATH

Makes 1 Bath

1 cup white wine   1 tablespoon rosemary
1 teaspoon ground ginger   10 drops jasmine oil

Mix all ingredients, cover container, and let stand in refrigerator for 24 hours. Strain before adding to bath. A tantalizing summer cooler.

WINTER WINE BATH

Makes 1 Bath

1 cup port wine   ¼ teaspoon ground nutmeg
8 whole cloves   1 stick cinnamon
2 slices orange, with peel

Combine all ingredients in a covered container and let steep in refrigerator for 24 hours. Strain and pour into a warm tub for a spicy wintertime soak.

SALTS BATHS

SANDALWOOD AND SALTS

Makes 1 Bath

1 cup Epsom salts   5 teaspoons corn starch
1 tablespoon baking powder 10 drops sandalwood oil

Combine dry ingredients and stir in oil. Cover and keep dry until ready to use. Scents like a sandalwood forest.

CITRUS AND SALTS

Makes 1 Bath

1 cup Epsom salts
peel of lemon, orange or lime
5 drops lemon, orange or lime oil
few drops of yellow, orange or green food coloring

Mix salts, peelings and coloring. Cover and let steep for 24 hours. (Do not leave longer as peel will spoil.) Pour mixture under warm running water. Enjoy this tangy bath with a tall glass of lemonade, orange juice or limeade.

SALT SEA BATH

Makes 1 Bath

1 pound rock salt
1 tub full of tepid water

This bath is refreshing, invigorating and a good substitute for sea bathing. Salt baths should not be indulged in frequently as they are drying to the skin.

GRAIN BATH BAGS

OATMEAL BATH BAG

Makes 1 Bath

½ cup powdered oatmeal   1 tablespoon grated mild soap
1 tablespoon borax   10 drops musk oil

Mix ingredients in a bowl and place in bath bag. Creams your skin while you scrub.

PEACHES AND CREAM BATH BAG

Makes 1 Bath

3 tablespoons powdered almond meal
½ cup powdered oatmeal   ½ cup powdered skim milk
10 drops peach oil

Combine ingredients in bowl and place in bath bag for a peaches and cream complexion.

HERB AND MEAL BATH BAG

Makes 1 Bath

½ cup oatmeal   2 teaspoons dried rosemary
¼ cup bran   2 bay leaves, crushed

Place all ingredients in blender and blend mixture to a coarse powder. Place in bath bag. Add a few drops of rosemary oil for additional scent.

FRAGRANT BATH OILS

ALMOND MILK OIL

Makes 1 Bath

2 cups fresh milk
2 tablespoons almond oil
2 teaspoons almond extract

Combine ingredients thoroughly in a covered container. Pour into bath water for a gently soothing and delightfully fragrant soak.

PERFUMED BATH OIL

2 tablespoons per bath

¼ cup safflower oil
10 drops jasmine oil
1 tablespoon shampoo

Place ingredients in a covered container and shake well. A luscious treat for pampered soft skin.

FOAMING BUBBLE BATH

¼ cup per bath

2 tablespoons safflower oil
½ cup shampoo
10 drops watermelon oil

Shake oil, shampoo and fragrance in a covered container. Pour ¼ cup under running water. A tub full of billowy bubbles awaits you!

IN BATH FACIAL MASQUES

ORANGE AND HONEY MASQUE

¼ cup powdered oatmeal   3 teaspoons honey
½ teaspoon water   4 drops orange oil

Place ingredients in a bowl and blend into a creamy paste. (Add a little more water if necessary.) Smooth onto clean face and neck. Leave masque on for 20 minutes. Rinse off with warm water, followed by a cool splash. Good for normal, dry and oily skin.

AVOCADO AND YOGURT MASQUE

½ small avocado, peeled
¼ cup yogurt

Mash avocado thoroughly until it is completely free of lumps. Stir in yogurt. Apply to clean face and neck and leave on for 20 minutes. Good for normal and dry skin.

PAPAYA TONING MASQUE

½ small papaya, peeled
1 egg white
½ teaspoon lemon juice

Place all ingredients in blender and blend until creamy smooth. Apply to clean face and neck. Leave on for 20 minutes. Remove with cool water and rinse with astringent. Good for normal and oily skin.

AFTER BATH SPLASHES

FLORIDA WATER

1 cup red rose petals
2 cups vodka
2 tablespoons dried sweet basil
2 tablespoons dried rosemary
2 tablespoons whole cloves
2 sticks cinnamon

8 drops rose oil
8 drops lavender oil
1 teaspoon lemon oil
8 drops orange oil
½ teaspoon light musk oil
½ teaspoon jasmine oil

Place petals in 1 cup vodka. Cover and let steep 1 week. Strain, cover and set aside. In pan pour 1 cup vodka and add basil, rosemary, cloves and cinnamon. Simmer over low heat for 15 minutes. Cover and let stand 24 hours. Strain 3 times through filter paper. (Any filter paper used for making coffee). Pour into rose petal vodka mixture and add oils. Cover and store in refrigerator. Shake before using. Splash on after bathing for a titillating tingle.

HUNGARY WATER

2 cups rose water
2 cups spirits of wine (brandy)
2 tablespoons mint leaves, crushed
½ cup dried rosemary
3 tablespoons lemon peel
4 tablespoons orange peel

Combine all ingredients and let steep 1 week in refrigerator. Strain 3 times through filter paper. (Any filter paper used for making coffee). Cover and store in refrigerator. Shake before using. A refreshing after bath splash for all seasons.

A BATH FOR ALL REASONS

STEAM AND SAUNA

One of the most exhilarating
and restorative experiences in the
lexicon of ablution is the steam bath,
enjoyed in ancient and modern times
from Rome to Helsinki.

The Romans took their steam baths in the *calidarium,* and the great bathing establishments of Islam always included a steam room. Turkish baths are world famous. Even in the blistering heat of the Sudan, the Sudanese squats in his hut, wrapped in a blanket, perspiring freely in a cloud of fragrant smoke from a wood fire.

American Indians also have steam baths. Early Indian sweat lodges were small arched huts, made with a stick frame and covered with a mixture of mud, pine needles and grass to keep in the steam. The plains Indians used a covering of buffalo hides. Today the Indians pile rugs, canvas or blankets up to one foot thick over the frame. Sweat lodges are usually located near a stream or lake so the steam bath can be followed by a water bath. Inside the hut a pit is dug and filled with hot rocks. Water is then splashed on the rocks, giving off a high-temperature steam vapor. Like the baths of ancient Rome, the Middle Ages and modern Finland, the Indian sweat baths are also social centers of communal bathing. In some tribes, refusal to bathe with a friend is taken as an insult. The Indians believe that steam baths remove evil spirits from the body.

The first use of steam for treating disease in the United States occurred in 1796, when Dr. Samuel Thompson of New England treated his daughter for an ailment that other physicians had been unable to cure. Since that time, steam bathing has acquired a strong following of devotees and health enthusiasts.

A steam bath cleanses like no other form of bathing. The pores open wide and perspiration is profuse. Hot steam stimulates circulation and improves skin tone. Steam bathing is *especially effective* for relieving sore muscles resulting from strenuous physical exercise. The therapeutic effect is immediate and dramatic, leaving you thoroughly relaxed and sparkling clean.

The most widely acclaimed steam bath is the Finnish sauna (pronounced *sowna*). Unlike the high humidity Turkish or Russian bath, the sauna produces a dry heat. Humidity rarely exceeds 10 percent, making the 140 to 240 degree temperatures more bearable. These extreme temperatures are amazing when you consider that the boiling point of water is 212 degrees F.

...the vapour bath is infinitely superior to the warm bath for all the purposes for which a warm bath can be given. An effective vapour bath may easily be had in any house at little cost and trouble.
— Encyclopedia Britannica, 1854

Finnish saunas are usually located in a wooden building detached from the main part of the house, and often near a lake or stream. They contain wood-burning stoves to heat the stones and wooden benches situated on two levels. The lower bench is for washing; the higher one for reclining in the hotter air close to the ceiling. In Finland, where one out of every six Finns has a sauna, the bath is a traditional Saturday night family affair.

The Finn begins his sauna by sitting or lying on the lower benches. In a few minutes he begins to perspire. When water is thrown on the hot igneous stones, a super-heated, invisible, skin-tingling steam is produced. The moisture is quickly absorbed into the wooden walls, maintaining a dry, comfortable atmosphere. This watering of the rocks, called *löyly,* is repeated several times in a 30 minute sauna. Soon the bather moves up to the higher, hotter bench and lies down. In a dry sauna, when the temperature reaches 180 degrees, skin temperature rises to about 110. Due to the high humidity produced immediately after the water-throwing, skin temperature can rise to 120 degrees. Normally, skin temperature is about 93 degrees.

During the sauna the family takes turns beating one another with birch whisks which have been softened by soaking in warm water. Birch-beating loosens the dead skin, stimulates circulation and releases an exhilarating scent. After the sauna, the robust Finns go jump in the lake or roll in the snow. They always follow-up with at least 15 minutes rest. A two hour sauna, consisting of several "baths", interspersed with brisk showers, skinny dips and relaxation, is not uncommon in Finland.

Cures without drugs! Every home should have our New Improved Thermal Vapor Bath Cabinet (patented.) It gives a hot vapor bath which forces all impurities from the system by natural action of the pores of the skin. Immediate relief guaranteed!
— American advertisement, 1898

Sauna bathing is gaining immense popularity in the United States as more and more Americans are having home saunas installed. Home saunas come in a variety of prices, materials and sizes. Almost any space may be utilized—closets, attics or cellars. Costs range from $800 for a pre-cut, 4 by 6 foot sauna kit to around $2500 for a large poolside sauna with shower and dressing room. Tile and asbestos-cement board are used, although pine, cedar and redwood have better moisture-absorbing qualities. Prefabricated, pre-cut saunas are available for do-it-yourself builders or they can be custom built to your own specifications. Gas and electric heaters have replaced the wood-burning Finnish stove. There is even a waterless "sauna" that uses an electric heater and an air-circulating fan. Rounding out the sauna experience are the various accessories available, from wooden water buckets and dippers to sauna sandals and Scandinavian sauna soap.

THE JAPANESE BATH

Stroll through a Japanese garden, study a Japanese print, or steep in a Japanese bath, and you will experience the essence of tranquility.

In Japan, a country flowing with natural hot springs and over 23,000 communal bathhouses, the bath has occupied a traditional place of honor. Bathing borders on ritual. In stark contrast to the West, where rushed showers are often the rule, the Japanese prefer a long, leisurely soak. A scalding bath in water up to 115 degrees is the ultimate refreshment, to be enjoyed in the company of one's family and friends: not alone, behind locked doors, as is the Western custom. To bathe in the same room where one eliminates is repugnant to Japanese sensitivity. Soaking oneself in a tubful of dirty, soapy water is equally distasteful. The American bathes to get clean: the Japanese gets clean in order to bathe.

The private bath *(ofuro)* is usually taken before dinner by all members of the family in order of their traditional importance— from the eldest male, down to the male servants, then the female members of the household. Most bathtubs are made of beautifully grained wood, which harmonizes with the rest of the house. Soaping and rinsing are always done outside the tub, followed by a tranquil soak in clean water.

The public bath *(sento)* is a necessity in Japan, where more than half of the homes still have no private bathing facilities. Even those who have bathrooms rarely use them because the cost of heating the water is prohibitive. Instead, they use the public baths for about 20 cents. The *sento* is also a social gathering place where the news of the day and gossip are exchanged. Whether public or private, the main functions of the Japanese bath are health and *relaxation.* In Japan, relaxation is a highly cultivated art.

Western eyebrows have a tendency to rise at mention of the Japanese communal bath. This is because the history of bathing in the West is closely connected with the history of sex. In most Western cultures, nudity is sexually provocative, in bath or out, while in Japan nudity at the bath is taken completely for granted. There exists a curious modesty at the *sento:* the nude body is not flaunted, and it is considered impolite to stare. Nudes are seen, but not looked at. Separate dressing rooms are provided for men and women. In many contemporary *sentos,* especially in the large cities, the bathers are sexually segregated. All in all, the Japanese co-ed bath is a most decorous experience.

After undressing, you are given a bar of soap and a small towel. The towel is wielded with skilled discretion for covering what the Japanese consider the most private part of the body. Soaping and rinsing (from a bucket) are done at a tap about 18 inches off the floor. During the soaping and rinsing one squats or sits discreetly on a wooden stool. The towel is used as a washcloth, then rinsed for drying. In the bath, a casual and relaxed air prevails. People take turns scrubbing each other's backs, and conversation is animated. Any feelings of embarrassment are washed away in the numbing embrace of piping hot water. Drying is done with one's back to the room.

Dirty-bath-water
  Where can I pour you?...insects
singing in the grass
                              — Onitsura

A remarkably proficient people, the Japanese are constantly improving on their baths. One innovation is the "Cable Car Bath" at the Arita Kanko Hotel on the seacoast south of Osaka. Here you bathe in sexually segregated tubs of hot, bubbling spa water mixed with concentrated orange juice, milk or sake. You soak for

awhile, then slip down a two story "slide bath" to the cable car loading platform. Each car has ten large tubs filled with plain hot water. Snugly submerged in the tub, you begin a scenic, watery ride to a lofty peak some 460 feet above the hotel. Private cable cars are available for couples, families and groups.

Another, drier, Japanese innovation is a sawdust bath popular in Yokohama, reputed to cure everything from asthma to sterility. Mixed into the sawdust are enzymes which remain in a constant state of fermentation. Buried up to his neck in sawdust, the "bather" sweats and ferments in scorching temperatures as high as 140 degrees. Obviously, this unusual bath is not intended for cleanliness.

Wet or dry, moving or static, the Japanese bath remains typically, magnificently, Oriental. East is East, and West is West, and if ever the twain meet we hope it will be in the tranquility of a Japanese *sento.*

SITZ, BIDET & WHIRLPOOL BATHS

Two baths, similar in function, are the bidet and sitz bath. Both involve perineal cleansing, although the sitz bath is primarily therapeutic in effect.

The sitz bath is believed to have been a Viking invention. *Sitz* is a German word, simply meaning "to sit". A sitz bath is taken by either sitting or squatting with only your vital parts immersed in the water. If squatting seems uncomfortable, take solace in the fact that a patent is presently on file for a chair-type sitz bath with a hole in the seat for bathing.

A popular sitz bath for men in Bavaria, called the Youth Bath, consists of immersing the scrotum in ice cold water for from one to two minutes. This is said to increase local circulation. It will certainly make a new man of you! Cool water sitz baths should not be taken for more than five minutes in about a half tub of water. The cooler the water, the more stimulating the bath. Hot sitz baths, taken the same way, are helpful in relieving the pains of hemorrhoids, menstrual cramps, bladder inflammation and pilonidal cysts.

The bidet, from the French "small horse", is designed for douching and perineal cleansing, and can also substitute as a sitz bath or footbath. Although common in Europe and Latin America, the bidet is relatively unknown to Americans. Many an American has pondered the bidet in a French bathroom, wondering exactly *what* to do with it. During World War I, American doughboys were introduced to the bidet by French prostitutes who douched with the bidet's fountain spray after coitus. This noble monument to feminine hygiene became a snickering subject, an object of ridicule, jibes and jokes. The result of this smear campaign was that no respectable American would be caught dead with one in his bathroom. In the early 1900's, the Ritz Carlton Hotel in New York was forced to remove its bidets by the outraged citizenry. Fortunately, the bidet is now beginning to reappear in the more sophisticated American bathrooms.

Should bathing the privates arise
Whatever the length, shape or size
   The bidet is fun
   To get the job done—
And for washing the feet takes the prize.
                            —Mal Whyte

Another therapeutic-type bath renowned for its refreshing effects is the whirlpool. Jacuzzi, perhaps the best known name in whirlpools, was invented by Candido Jacuzzi, a turbine and jet pump manufacturer, after doctors had prescribed water massage for his arthritic son. Since at the time whirlpools were only available in hospitals, Jacuzzi designed a portable hydromassage for home treatment. Home whirlpools are now available in portable models or permanently built-in versions. Some have a flexible hose attachment for local massaging of head, neck, shoulders and limbs. The aerated water bubbles and swirls, caressing your body in its soothing embrace, while tensions disappear in a frothy foam.

Whirlpools are used extensively by physical therapists and hospitals for treatment of arthritis, rheumatism, polio, bone and muscle injuries and a host of other bodily aches and pains. A whirlpool bath is excellent for stimulating local circulation and relaxing tired muscles. If you plan to install a whirlpool for a particular ailment, be sure to consult your doctor for advice on which type would be best for you.

THE HEALTH SPAS

Discovered by the Romans, perfected by the Europeans, and adopted by the Americans, the spa has attracted health-seekers from ancient to modern times. Its ages old popularity springs from our unwavering belief in the curative powers of water.

As the Roman legions tramped across Europe, they stopped to refresh their war-weary bones in the bubbling wellsprings of the continent, from Bath to Aix to Baden-Baden. There they built magnificent temples and spas in honor of the gods. Bath, in England, was called *Aquae Sulis* (the waters of Minerva) by the Romans. By 75 A.D., Bath was swimming with Roman patricians. Lost after the Roman occupation, the thermal pools of Bath were rediscovered in the 12th century. A legend originated at the time explaining that the springs were first discovered by Prince Baldud, the sire of King Lear. Baldud, a leper, was banished to the hills, where he became a swineherd. One day his pigs toppled into the pools by accident and emerged much improved in health. Following their lead, Baldud took the waters himself and his leprosy was immediately cured.

Since then, the European spas have been used in the treatment of various and sundry ills ranging from arthritis and nervous exhaustion to bronchitis and gynecological disorders. Heart trouble, brain damage, bone and blood problems have all been brought to the magical springs. Many of the waters are abundant in iron, magnesium, sulphur, carbonic acid, salts and arsenic, reputed to do wonders for sterility and barrenness. Mary, Queen of James II, credited her long sought motherhood to the "fecundating springs" of Cross Bath. Some waters are even said to be radioactive.

Spas are named after the town of Spa, Belgium, where mineral springs were discovered in 1326. The great European spas reached their pinnacle of popularity in the 18th century when a steady stream of royalty and elite came to "take the waters." Napoleon drank and soaked in Vichy water. Queen Victoria favored the waters at Aix-les-Bains, while Edward VII was a habitué of Baden-Baden. Marie Antoinette was told by her doctors not to bathe during her menstrual period. In sympathy, Louis XVI decreed that the spas must work their treatments in three weeks, with the result that today in Vittel the "cure" lasts 21 days.

Oh! 'twas a glorious sight to behold the fair sex
  All wading with gentlemen up to their necks,
And view them so prettily tumble and sprawl
  In a big smoking kettle as big as our hall.
                    — *Anstey's* **Bath Poetical Guide**

These last resorts of royalty became the playgrounds of the Western world, famed as centers of social intercourse. During the day one took the waters; at night one took to the gaming tables, ballrooms and dining halls. The game of E & O, from which modern roulette is derived, was first played at the English spas in 1739. Today the casinos are still very much a part of the European spas at Bath, Droitwich, Royal Leamington, Vichy, Vittel, Evian, Divonne, Wiesbaden, Kissingen and others. The games include baccarat, chemin de fer and, of course, roulette. All manner of sports are also enjoyed. Golf, tennis, boating, hunting, skeet shooting and horse racing provide a sportsman's paradise. All is not sport, however. The Europeans take their spas with overflowing seriousness. In Russia, a country with over 2500 spas, a new science, called koorotology, for the German *kurort* (health resort), has been developed.

In America, the Indians had discovered the healing effects of the natural hot springs long before Ponce de León arrived in search of the Fountain of Youth. Hundreds of mineral springs dot the American landscape from Stafford Springs, Connecticut to Palm Springs, California. Stafford Springs was discovered by the Nipmuck Indians; Palm Springs by the Agua Caliente (hot water) tribe. Like the Romans, the Indians believed the springs contained miraculous healing powers, and they made them centers of sacred ceremonies.

Taking their cue from the Europeans, the Americans in the 19th century built vast Victorian pleasure domes on the sites of the springs. In their heyday, spas like French Lick, Hot White Sulphur Springs and Saratoga rivaled their European counterparts as places where the elite came to spend the season in and around the bubbling pools. As far back as the 1700's, dignitaries like Washington, Jefferson and Hamilton soaked in the Virginia Springs.

Suvarnanabha claims that all complicated and difficult positions and acts, whether performed sitting, standing or lying, should first be tried in water, as this facilitates access and renders it possible to master these difficult though pleasurable techniques.
— Kama Sutra

Today, in our super health-conscious society, the spas are enjoying a national revival, and are a major part of the entire health industry. The emphasis has shifted slightly from a strictly medical aspect to one of beauty care and general health.

In most health spas and beauty farms, the "cure" begins with a complete physical examination, followed by a personalized treatment schedule which includes hot mineral baths, cold showers, mud baths, sunbathing, steam, sauna, herbal wraps, massage, exercise and yoga. Even the menu may be designed with the weight-conscious in mind, offering salt-free, low cholesterol and protein diets. Also included are programs for outdoor exercise ranging from horseback riding to jogging, and, naturally, swimming. Some spas are co-ed; others are sexually segregated. The more luxurious health spas cost between $500 and $1000 per week, continuing the elitist tradition of the bath. Many offer admittance by membership only.

As more and more Americans are faced with increased leisure time, the spas' popularity will continue to grow. Where else can you have such good, clean fun?

THE BATHROOM

DECORATING THE BATHROOM

Your bathroom is the most intimate,
personal room in your home.
This room,
above all others,
will reflect your life style
at its most basic level.

The function of the bathroom, and our attitude toward it, are rapidly changing. Bathrooms no longer need to be small, dreary, dull places. After all, many hours are spent in this room on health and grooming. New, moderate priced housing is being designed incorporating large, multi-equipped areas around the bathroom.

I have had a good many more uplifting thoughts, creative and expansive visions ...in well-equipped American bathrooms than I have ever had in any cathedral.
— Edmund Wilson

Home spas, which include steam and sauna baths, large or sunken tubs and sun lamps, are the trend. If these features fit into your life style, fit them into your remodeling plans and budget. Whether large or small, new or remodeled, the bathroom must be functional. In addition, it must be sanitary, easy to clean and attractive to behold.

Before you begin redecorating the bathroom, consider how you live. Do you rent? Plan to build? Redecorate your existing room? How many people will use the bathroom? Are they adults or children? If you are purchasing permanent fixtures, you must plan for the present *and* the future. A comprehensive, concise plan is the key to successful decorating, whether in the bathroom or any other room in the house.

Begin by making an accurate floor plan. The eight foot tub you might admire will never fit into a seven foot space. Purchase graph paper that is marked off in 1/4 inch squares. Each square represents one square foot. Carefully measure and draw the room to scale. Note everything in it: doors, windows, permanent fixtures, heating registers, built-ins, cabinets. Note all electrical outlets. When your floor plan is complete, develop and arrange your room step by step. Everything will fall into place with a system. Don't rush! A little patience will result in a functional and attractive bathroom. To eliminate costly mistakes, always carry your floor plan with you when shopping for materials.

Only you can determine which decor suits your needs. If you have no particular decorating ideas in mind, take several tours of your local bath boutiques and department stores. Look through books and magazines and check advertisements. Save clippings and start a decorating file.

Every room sets a mood and a style. Establish your own personal mood and style and your decorating experience will be a rewarding one. Formal or casual, bright or subdued, the choice is yours.

SETTING A MOOD

There is no absolute rule for setting a mood in modern decorating. Be innovative. Select a focal point, such as a mirrored wall, and build around it. Neutral fixtures are the easiest to work with. Add color with towels, window dressings, rugs and other accessories. These things wear out faster than tubs, lavatories, toilets and flooring. A red bathtub may be attractive today, but difficult to decorate around tomorrow. Drab colors are out. Select appointments for the bathroom as you would for the bedroom, living or dining rooms.

COLOR

Color is the most important consideration in interior decorating. Step into any setting and the first thing that affects you is color. In the early stages of your planning, decide on the color scheme you wish to use. The language of color is easy to learn. Develop a basic color vocabulary and explore color everywhere. Nature is a window to the world of color. Study nature to learn how the colors of the natural world blend and contrast. Bring the colors of nature into the bathroom with some of the many plants that thrive in a humid bathroom atmosphere.

Warm colors—reds, oranges, yellows—are aggressive and demand attention. They give vital brightness to cold, dark bathrooms. Bold, warm colors are excellent in rooms with high ceilings. A large area of warm color will make your bathroom appear smaller. Cool colors—greens, blues, purples—are serene and restful. Decorate in cool colors to make your bathroom appear larger. Cool colors show best in well lighted rooms.

LIGHTING

In addition to spotlighting your decor, a well-lighted bathroom is necessary for safety, personal hygiene and cosmetic reasons. The trend is toward functional lighting and attractive fixtures. Whether direct or indirect, lighting should be soft and non-glare. The light should not cast shadows unless they are desired for special effect. If your bathroom lighting is inadequate, the use of light colors, glossy surfaces and mirrors will help reflect the available light. The area around mirrors should be especially well lighted for good grooming.

CEILINGS

An attractive ceiling is an important consideration in the smart bathroom. The ceiling is often forgotten—overlooked, as it were—but with the many materials available today this need not be so. Specially designed grilled panels can be installed and lighted from above to give your bathroom a dramatic glow. Wallpaper will cover blemishes and add color to a ceiling. Beamed ceilings can be matched with wallpaper or used alone. Wood beams may be painted or stained. Decorative moldings will add a finishing touch to the beauty overhead.

WALLS

A fresh coat of paint is the easiest and least expensive way to add color to your bathroom. The right hues can turn a rather dull room into a cheery setting. Good quality paint is a must for the bathroom. The paint must be washable, moistureproof, stain and fade resistant. When purchasing paint, keep in mind the delicate interplay of color and light. Color changes under different light. Be sure to view the colors you plan to use under the lighting conditions in which they will appear. Cool light emanates from the north and east; warm light from the south and west. Try to find the balance between the existing light and the intensity of wall coloring. Color will appear more intense and vibrant on a large area than on a small one. Therefore, when painting a large wall area, it is a good idea to use lighter hues. If you know a good painter, have him paint the walls with a custom design or in supergraphics.

Fiberglass Wall Units

Fiberglass wall units are setting a trend in the bathroom. This extremely durable material is soft and warm to the touch, resists odor, mildew, and bacterial growth and is easy to clean and install. New products are available with interchangeable color panels. Fiberglass is ideal in bathrooms where other materials are impractical or expensive.

Paneled Walls

Paneling is becoming increasingly popular in bathroom decor. The many designs, textures, colors and patterns available give the decorator innumerable choices. Choose paneling that is easy to install and keep clean. It should be water and scratch resistant. You can either use the paneling alone as a total wall covering, or combine it with paint and wallpaper.

Tiled Walls

Tile has many advantages—and disadvantages—in the bathroom. It is long-lasting, durable and moisture resistant. At the same time, it is somewhat difficult to clean, cold to the touch and expensive. Here again, it is your personal preference and budget that determine the choice between tile and some of the more contemporary wall coverings.

If you are not satisfied with the color of your existing tile and it is difficult to replace, work around it. Play up a complementary or contrasting color. All white tile, for example, will have style when contrasted with black accessories. Add mirrors and chrome for a polished look. If the tile is two-toned, pick up one color and coordinate it with paint and wallpaper. Colorful walls will draw the eye away from the tile. To avoid a busy effect, do not combine more than two or three colors.

Wallpaper

There are hundreds of wallpaper patterns available to fit every budget, mood and decor, so be prepared to spend some time in your selection. Specially coated, textured and flocked papers are available in water resistant, canvas-backed vinyls. There is even a "scrubbable flocked" paper that withstands scrubbing with the strongest soap. Patterns should be chosen for their functional as well as decorative value. Stripes can be a bold accent to a large or small room. Vertical stripes will make the bathroom appear taller; horizontal stripes will give a wider appearance to a narrow bathroom. If you paper an entire room—walls and ceilings—it will make the room look larger by eliminating the ceiling angles. A small, dark pattern will close in a room. To enlarge a room, use a floating pattern on a light background.

Before purchasing wallpaper, check it against the background and under the lighting conditions in which you plan to use it.

FLOORS

Neglecting an old or worn bathroom floor is no longer necessary with the many choices of beautiful coverings to match every style and period bathroom. Shop and study the advantages and disadvantages of all types of covering.

Carpeting

Wall to wall bath carpeting is popular with those who desire softness and warmth at their feet. Carpet is also convenient when you do not want the mess or expense of installing a new floor. Good quality carpet is a wise investment for the bathroom. Hygienic reasons demand that you select a material that will withstand many washings and dryings. Because of bathroom dampness, look for carpeting that will not rot or mildew. Carpet should not curl. It should be easy to vacuum. Bath rugs can be laid on top of carpeting for sanitary reasons around the toilet, tub or under lavatories. These can be changed often, minimizing the need for frequent washing of the larger carpet. You can match wall to wall carpeting with small rugs, tank and seat covers, tissue boxes and waste baskets.

Ceramic Tile

Tile is long wearing, moisture resistant and extremely attractive. It is especially luxurious, in lieu of marble, around large sunken tubs. Dark grouting has become very popular in recent years. It can be kept clean and sanitary without excess scrubbing. Do not use bleaching products near dark grouted tile.

Vinyl

New vinyl floor coverings are being manufactured in a rainbow of colors, patterns and designs. Many are cushioned for extra softness and never need waxing. This no-wax type of flooring is excellent in the bathroom, where there is always the danger of slipping. Many products are easy to install for the do-it-yourselfer. Be careful not to drop sharp pointed objects on vinyl as it might chip or dent. Check with the store to find out which cleaning agent is best to use. Harsh abrasives may dull the shine.

WINDOWS

Traditionally, bathroom windows were covered with vinyl curtains decorated with swans, seascapes and fish. Today, window dressings range from Roman shades to exotic shoji screens. The two basic considerations for the bathroom window are privacy and easy care. Once these considerations have been met, choose a covering that will enhance your decor. Small, unattractive windows are less noticeable if they are made to blend into the entire wall. This is easily achieved by matching curtain material with wallpaper or paint. A laminated shade will produce the same effect. Small windows can be made to appear larger by extending the moldings and trimmings. If you plan to change your decor often, select panel-type fabric shutters. Just replace the fabric for a new look or color scheme. Curtain adjusting rods can play a multiple role in the bathroom. Use matching rods for curtains, towel bars and shower curtains to achieve an integrated effect.

BATHROOM ACCESSORIES

BATH MATS
Bath mats have been used since medieval times to insulate the floor from drips, and the bather from the floor. Bath mats *must* be non-slip. The pile should be thick, with maximum absorbency. Never substitute a throw rug for a bath mat.

BATH MITTS AND STRAPS
The bath mitt was originally used after drying as a massage glove. Today, these scrubbing aids are made from a variety of materials from hemp and horsehair to loofah and terrycloth. Bath straps are excellent for scrubbing backs and bottoms. Pour some of your favorite bath oil or friction lotion on your mitt, strap (or brush) and scrub away.

BATH PILLOWS
Bath pillows provide cushioned comfort when soaking. They come in a multitude of sizes, shapes, and colors and are usually made from foam rubber or inflatable plastic. The inflatable types are easiest to store. A rolled up towel can also serve as a comfortable bath pillow.

BATHING MODULES
Acrylic and fiberglass bathing modules are designed to fit almost any available space. They come in solo tub or shower stall models, or complete with tub, shower, bath seats, towel bars, safety grips and shelves all in one cornerless, compact unit. Bathing modules are easy to install and maintain, and are relatively inexpensive.

BATHROOM DISPENSER
Push button liquid dispensers are ideal for storing soaps, lotions,

creams, oils and shampoos. Some have separate compartments for storing several liquids. Bathroom dispensers can be conveniently mounted on the bath or shower wall.

BRUSHES
A brisk brushing is good for cleansing and stimulating circulation. Brushes with soft, medium or stiff bristles range in size from the large, masculine Turkish bath brush to delicate feminine face brushes. Some have long handles for brushing hard to reach places; others have no handles at all. There are even brushes with rubber bristles and brushes that float!

LOOFAH
A loofah is the dried seed pod of a tropical gourd. Its abrasive texture makes it excellent for scrubbing. Some are tailored to mitten shapes. A vigorous scrub with a loofah cleans, promotes circulation and leaves you with a rosy glow. You can even grow your loofah right in your own back yard!

PERSONAL SHOWERS
Personal showers are a European innovation, consisting of a portable shower head mounted on a flexible hose. Most feature push button, finger-tip controls. The head can be mounted on the wall like a regular shower or hand-held. Ideal for personal hygiene, local body bathing and cleaning the tub or shower after bathing.

PUMICE
These light, mouse-shaped pieces of volcanic rock are used for removing calluses and roughness on feet and around fingernails. Be sure to wet the pumice before using.

SAFETY GRIP BARS
All bathtubs and showers should be equipped with safety grip

bars. These bars can be permanently fastened to shower walls or to the edge of the tub. Safety bars are especially recommended for the physically handicapped and the elderly.

SAUNA TENTS AND SUITS

For those who can't afford a built-in sauna, there are inexpensive sauna tents, or bags, complete with steam generator, that operate on house current. In one model, priced under $13, the bather sits with only his head outside the bag while his body steams inside. Heat sealing sauna suits can be worn while working around the house for an effective sweat bath.

SHOWER CURTAINS

Shower curtains come in hanging or door-type styles in a wide array of colors and designs. Matching curtain and towel combinations are available to complement any decor. Some shower curtains have built-in, self-draining pockets to hold bathing accessories. Although they are usually made of vinyl, other fabrics, such as cotton, are also used.

SHOWER CURTAIN HOLDERS

For splashers who can't seem to keep the water in the shower, there are several clip devices to hold the shower curtain taut at the sides and bottom. Some fasten with magnets; others are self-stick. Happy splashing!

SHOWER HEADS

The numerous shower heads on the market provide a variety of features to enhance your bath. Some can be filled with bath oils, liquid soaps or bubble bath for a bubble shower. Others are equipped with water-conserving regulator valves and aerators to reduce water pressure. Special shower heads pulsate streaming jets of water or a spiraling, whirlpool stream to massage aching muscles. One manufacturer offers a 24 karat gold-plated shower head; another, a "shoulder shower" that fits around the neck, only wetting the body from the shoulders down. Great for avoiding a wet head!

SOAP DISHES

Soap dishes are functional, decorative necessities for the bath. Dishes mounted on suction cups can be moved around the bathroom. One manufacturer offers a magnetic soap dish with a guarantee that the soap won't "budge an inch from its container no matter how wet". For those who can't tolerate soap dishes, there is always soap-on-a-rope.

SPONGES

Sponges may be either natural or synthetic. Natural sponges, essential for luxurious bathing, come in several shapes, sizes and textures. You can caress your face with a superfine silk sponge or use a large elephant's ear sponge in place of a washcloth. Special sponges are available for removing corns and calluses. There is a long-handled sponge brush that holds soap for back scrubbing.

THERMOMETERS

For safety and comfort, always use a bath thermometer when bathing in extreme water temperatures. It will help you to maintain the constant, even temperature you desire. Do not attempt to substitute a medical thermometer in place of a bath thermometer.

TOWELS

Towels come in numerous colors, materials and sizes, from tiny finger towels to giant bath sheets. They should be both functional and decorative. Terrycloth towels are still the most popular, because of their absorbency, thick pile and luxurious feel, although synthetic polyester and cotton blends are also available. Your home should have at least six face and six bath towels per person. For the ultimate luxury, try toasting your towel in a heated towel rack before drying.

TUB SAFETY TREADS

A must for safety, tub treads are non-skid mats or adhesive strips designed to prevent slipping in the tub or shower. They are sold in a variety of colors, patterns and shapes to blend in with your bath decor. Some tub treads come with matching applique designs for the shower door. Special waterproof, skidproof slippers are also available to help prevent accidents.

TUB SEATS

Tub seats are convenient for footbaths and foot soaking, as well as for overall body lathering. In the absence of a bidet, bathtub seats can also be used when douching.

TUB TRAYS

Tub trays fit across the bathtub to hold anything from manicure tools and cosmetics to magazines or a cool drink. Excellent for people who like to do things while bathing.

WASHCLOTHS

We recommend using two washcloths, preferably terrycloth: one for the face and neck, the other for the torso. Each person in the house should have four pairs of washcloths. Washcloths should also be decorative and either mix or match with towels and the overall bath decor.

SELECTED BIBLIOGRAPHY

Amory, Cleveland. *The Last Resorts.* New York: Harper & Brothers, Publishers, 1948.

Barbeau, A. *Life & Letters at Bath in the XVIIIth Century.* New York: Dodd, Mead & Company, 1904.

Bramson, Ann Sela. *Soap. Making It, Using It, Enjoying It.* New York: Workman Publishing Company, 1972.

Brauer, Earle W., M.D., *Your Skin and Hair: A Basic Guide to Care and Beauty.* New York: The Macmillan Company, 1969.

Castle, Molly. *How To Be 30 For Forty Years.* New York: Dodd, Mead & Company, 1962.

Cooley, Arnold J. *The Toilet In Ancient and Modern Times.* New York: Burt Franklin, 1970. Originally published in 1866.

Elder, Leon. *Hot Tubs.* Santa Barbara: Capra Press, 1973.

Ellis, Aytoun. *The Essence of Beauty.* New York: The Macmillan Company, 1960.

Harry, Ralph G. *Modern Cosmeticology.* New York: Chemical Publishing Company, 1962. Vol. I.

Hauser, Gayelord. *Mirror, Mirror on the Wall.* New York: Farrar, Straus and Cudahy, 1961.

Hauser, Gayelord. *Treasury Of Secrets.* Greenwich, Conn.: A Fawcett Crest Book, 1951.

Hopkins, Albert A. (Ed.). *The Scientific American Cyclopedia of Receipts, Notes and Queries.* New York: Munn & Co., Publishers, 1892.

Kira, Alexander. *The Bathroom: Criteria for Design.* New York: Bantam Books, Inc., 1966.

Poucher, William A. *Perfume, Cosmetics and Soaps.* London: Chapman and Hall Ltd., 1959. 3 Vols.

Rutledge, Deborah. *Natural Beauty Secrets.* New York: Avon Books, 1967.

Stepat-De Van, Dorothy. *Introduction to Home Furnishings.* New York: The Macmillan Company, 1964.

Sternberg, Thomas H., M.D. *More Than Skin Deep.* Garden City, N.Y.: Doubleday & Company, Inc., 1970.

Uggams, Leslie. *The Leslie Uggams Beauty Book.* Englewood Cliffs, N.J.: Prentice-Hall, Inc., 1966.

Wellman, Katharine. *Beauty Begins At Home.* New York: Covici, Friede Publishers, 1936.

Wright, Lawrence. *Clean and Decent.* New York: The Viking Press, 1960.

PROFESSIONAL JOURNALS

De/Journal. (Monthly). Briarcliff Manor, N.Y.: Construction Industry Press, Inc.

Bath Products Merchandising. (Quarterly). Islip, New York: Dogan Publishing Company.

Contractor Magazine. (Bimonthly). Pittsfield, Mass.: Buttenheim Publishing Corporation.

Home Furnishings Daily. (Daily). New York: Fairchild Publications.

Linens, Domestics & Bath Products. (Bimonthly). New York: Columbia Communications.

INDEX

INDEX OF RECIPES